# PHILOSOPHICAL PROBLEMS IN HEALTH CARE

# Philosophical Problems in Health Care

*Edited by*
DAVID GREAVES
HUGH UPTON
*Centre for Philosophy and Health Care*
*University of Wales, Swansea*

# Ashgate

Aldershot • Brookfield USA • Singapore • Sydney

Published by
Ashgate Publishing Company
Gower House
Croft Road
Aldershot, Hants
GU11 3HR
England

Ashgate Publishing Company
Old PostRoad
Brookfield
Vermont 05036
USA

Ashgate website:http://www.ashgate.com

Reprinted 1997, 1999

A CIP catalogue record for this book is available from the British Library

**Library of Congress Catalog Card Number:** 95-83733

ISBN 1 85972 222 9

Typeset by
Neil Pickering
Centre for Philosophy and Health Care
University of Wales, Swansea
Singleton Park
Swansea SA2 9PP

Printed in Great Britain by Biddles Limited,
Guildford and King's Lynn

# Contents

# Preface

Several good introductory books on health care ethics are now available, but because their remit is to be comprehensive they inevitably tend to deal with the subject at a rather superficial level. The purpose of this volume is therefore to provide a different and complementary approach, still accessible to those engaging with the subject for the first time, but dealing with a selected range of important issues in greater depth, and encompassing conceptual as well as ethical concerns.

To try to achieve this we have asked each of the academic staff of the Centre for Philosophy and Health Care to prepare a chapter on a topic with which they are already familiar and which in most cases has already been the subject of their teaching to postgraduate students. We are particularly pleased that they have all agreed to contribute, so that the collection reflects the multidisciplinary character and interests of the Centre as a whole. Several of the staff involved are qualified in more than one discipline, but their original backgrounds were variously in philosophy, medicine, nursing, law, theology, political theory and literature.

The original inspiration for the book came from Don Evans, the Director of the Centre, and he has given us great encouragement at every stage. The arduous technical task of harmonising the scripts of twelve authors for publication has been carried out by Neil Pickering with his usual efficiency and cheerfulness.

# Introduction

In recent years there have been striking developments in the intellectual landscape lying between philosophy and health care. Philosophy, under such titles as applied philosophy, bioethics or applied ethics, has taken an increasing interest in issues of practical public concern, many of the issues being those arising in health care. Also, beside the ancient and continuing study of the concepts of disease and health in general, there has been a marked increase in work on the philosophy of psychiatry and psychopathology. On the other side, professionals working in the health services and related areas have gradually come to feel a need for the inclusion of the study of the moral aspects of their work in their training. Thus there has been a movement towards the study of medical and nursing ethics.

Given these variously titled, though often overlapping, areas of study, it is perhaps worth saying something of the genesis and purpose of this volume. Firstly, the chapters are intended to be introductory in nature. They have arisen from a number of years of teaching an MA course in the philosophy and ethics of health care to those professionals working in health care and other related services. They are thus intended to be accessible to this kind of reader, typically lacking any formal background in the study of philosophy. Secondly, the term 'health care' has been deliberately preferred to the more usual 'medical', both here and in our teaching. Much work of a similar kind is carried on under the title 'medical ethics', but there is a risk of this suggesting an artificial limitation to the area of study. It is true that this term is sometimes understood in a fairly broad sense, but equally it can sometimes reflect an important but narrow concern with the work of doctors, with what is morally permissible or impermissible for them, with the nature of their relations with their patients and with disease and its cure. Questions of nursing care, medical research and health policy may also involve conceptual or ethical problems, and take us beyond this narrow understanding of the

1

medical.

Something may also need saying on the preference for 'philosophical' over 'ethical' in the title. This is not to deny that many of our concerns are of an ethical kind, a point that would anyway soon become obvious to the reader. Nor is it to reject the usual assumption that medical and health care ethics are at least partly philosophical in nature, so that one could reasonably expect the use of 'ethics' to carry that implication with it in this context. Both of these still leave a further important matter of accurate terminology. There is at least one significant cluster of issues that we wanted to include that are not primarily ethical ones, namely those relating to our understanding of the very concepts of health, illness and disease, both mental and physical. Accuracy, then, demanded a title that would cover not just philosophical ethics, but other branches of philosophy as well. This, of course, leads to a somewhat deeper question; that of why both elements should be included in the teaching of health care professionals when the narrower scope of ethics is more often favoured.

One perfectly good reason is the inherent interest of studying the bearing of these other branches upon some of the central concepts of health care. In teaching those who are attracted to a philosophical approach to health care ethics there is good reason to assume that some will be stimulated by other philosophical issues as well. The general principles of a liberal education can surely have a place here as elsewhere. Nor need this be solely a matter of what is found intellectually stimulating, since breadth of study may well have a subtle effect on future professional practice. There is also, though, a compelling reason to broaden the enquiry even for those who think such principles a luxury and that all study in this area should directly and explicitly relate to practice. It is our belief that even if the aim was simply to study health care ethics, this would naturally lead one into conceptual questions that are not directly ethical. For example we can take something of obvious practical concern to those engaged in health care, namely the whole issue of the place of ethics in health care education. Although there is a trend, as mentioned above, towards its inclusion, the precise manner of this inclusion is debated. Is it, at one extreme, to be seen as an extra item to be added to an essentially empirical study of the practice of curing and healing, where ethics is regarded as a matter of behaving decently towards patients while carrying on the essentially scientific business of treating their disorders? Or are we to say that the whole enterprise of health care is a normative one, inescapably involving individual and collective judgements of value? There is no way of deciding this fundamental issue without some consideration of the nature of such concepts as health and disease, curing and caring; and no intellectually respectable way of teaching in this area without sharing these philosophical deliberations with the students.

2

Similarly if we look at the pressing questions of health policy. Many, for example, would find it plausible to suppose that a public health service must always give priority to treating conditions that are relatively urgent or severe, and above all to those involving a threat to life. Yet is the medical prolonging of life always to have priority or can this depend on what sort of life we are dealing with? If we think that the quality of a life is relevant, we may then have to judge whether the continuation of some life is worthwhile. In this case we would surely be irresponsible if we failed to ask such philosophical questions as what kind of judgement this might be and what, if anything, might make these judgements correct or incorrect. These are not, or not solely, questions of ethics, but must involve a wider discussion of what it is that makes a life worthwhile and of the various ways in which we might try to assess this in another. The ethical question of whether we ever have the right to do so is only one among many, and not necessarily the one we should try to answer first.

The claim, then, is that any study of health care ethics that is to avoid superficiality will be led into philosophy, and not just in the form of philosophical ethics but also of conceptual problems of a non-moral kind. If we take a general look at the structure of some standard examples, there seem, on the surface at least, to be two ways in which this may occur. It is a distinction that certainly colours the way in which this area of study is seen, though arguably it turns out not to be one of much depth.

One way in which philosophy may impinge occurs when our practical concerns require us to attempt a resolution of a question that is regarded as a purely philosophical problem. For example, when resources for public health care are in short supply there may be an understandable pressure to reconsider the status of some apparently marginal conditions to see whether they were arguably outside the scope of illness and disease, and thus not appropriate objects of funding. Clearly such moves cannot properly be made or contested without some study of the concepts of illness and disease, and specifically of whether they are concepts of a descriptive or evaluative nature. Nor will it be satisfactory for those making the decision wholly to delegate this study. At the very least they should be able to make an intelligent assessment of the accounts of these concepts.

The other way in which philosophy enters into health care is where a question that appears on the scene as clearly practical in nature turns out to have philosophical components embedded in it, where these do not already have the status of complete, pre-existing philosophical problems. Interestingly, some of these practical questions seem themselves to have acquired some kind of philosophical status, but it is still worth noting that there is a difference in the general structure in such cases. The problem of the permissibility of abortion is perhaps the best example. It has arisen as a practical, moral question but is now taught as part of some undergraduate philosophy courses and has been a prominent subject in philosophical journals for more than twenty years. Not surprisingly it has raised questions for moral philosophy, but our uncertainty about the status of the embryo and foetus means that it has raised them in conjunction with various metaphysical questions about potentiality, identity and personhood. So, in what way is the permissibility of abortion a problem for philosophy? Not, let us assume, in that philosophical reflection is all that rational people will require to produce an agreed answer. Of course, if this is true, so much the better for the importance of philosophy, but there is no need for us to make such a controversial claim. It is enough, surely, that the question of abortion contains elements that are philosophical and which must be addressed in any satisfactory resolution. In this way too, we may say, there are philosophical problems in health care.

It is a consequence of this view that the importance of philosophy in this area does not depend on its being the sole determinant of a solution in a given problem. For example, the problem of the permissibility of abortion will end with a person's moral judgement, one that is (again, let us assume) not wholly determined by the philosophical elements of the inquiry. On the other hand, if we take a different problem, one described as providing an analysis of the concept of disease, then this specific problem will begin and end as a philosophical one, whatever the practical ramifications of the result. Yet if in both cases philosophy is essential to a satisfactory attempt to find an answer, then it is as important to the one that appears to be purely a moral problem as it is to the more conspicuously conceptual one, despite the fact that it forms only an element of the first and the whole of the second.

The substantive details of exactly when, and to what degree, health care (or indeed any other of life's practical concerns) poses philosophical problems, ethical or otherwise, will inevitably be controversial; inevitably because the nature and scope of philosophy is itself, quite properly, disputed by its practitioners. Our primary aim in this volume has been to try to show the wide range of problems in health care that are either philosophical in nature or have a philosophical component. The subjects have been divided into three sections, with the first concentrating on personhood, the concept of care and the beginning and end of life. In this section we have introduced one exception to the philosophical focus in order to make reference to another body of thought that attempts an argued resolution to the same problems, namely the law. Nowhere in health care is the law more conspicuous and controversial than in matters of treatment and care at the end of life and, with some of the more prominent recent judgements showing obvious awareness of the same issues that have been taken up by philosophers, we asked the Centre's specialist on medical law to give an account of the current state of the law in this area. It will, we hope, provide a rich source for philosophical reflection as well as being informative in its own right.

In the second section, while not leaving the problem of the status of persons entirely behind, we move on to questions concerning what they suffer from and the basis of their treatment. Here the contributors discuss the concepts of health, illness and disease, the particular problem of the status of mental illness, our understanding of, and attitude towards, learning difficulties, and take a provocatively sceptical look at the important issue of alternative medicine. Finally we turn in the third section to health policy, to the general question of the role of the state in health care, the more specific problems of trying to calculate the right allocation resources, the scope of the idea of ethical review, and lastly the question of our responsibilities for health in the Third World.

What we hope to have provided is a wide-ranging selection covering the areas of the subject that we consider to be important, but without attempting to be comprehensive. Within this range it will be found that the contributors take diverse approaches to their subjects and also have various styles of presentation. Most of the chapters derive from lectures to and discussions with our students and we have not tried to impose any great degree of uniformity, on the assumption that just as students enjoy variety in teaching, so they may in writing. We would like to give warm thanks to our past students for what we have learnt in meeting with and teaching them and hope that this collection will be useful to those studying in this area in the future.

*David Greaves*
*Hugh Upton*

# Part One

# CARING AND THE BOUNDARIES OF LIFE

# 1 Caring intensively

*Louise de Raeve*

This chapter will focus on the concept of care in health care and in particular on intensive care from the perspective of nursing. However, much of what is said should be applicable to medicine and professions allied to medicine. By intensive care is meant those contexts of care where, either in virtue of the extent over time and/or in virtue of a high nurse to patient ratio, nurses have the opportunity to get to know their patients in a way that would not be possible in an outpatient, recovery or accident and emergency department. Before embarking on an exploration of the concept of care in a health/illness context, it seems necessary to examine the concept of care in general in order to see what similarities and differences may exist between lay care and professional health care.

In our every day lives we both *care for* (take care of) and *care about* many different things and we may be described as either *caring* or *uncaring* people. However, it isn't straightforwardly clear what if anything is the proper relationship between these three dimensions of care: its instrumental or behaviourial sense, its attitudinal sense and its dispositional sense. As a parent, I both care about and take care of my children. I cook and clean for them and I worry about their futures and I mind if they are ill or upset. However, if I stated that I cared about my children but then in practice consistently neglected them in every conceivable way, my caring about them would be considered suspect by others and I would probably be judged to be an uncaring mother.

This makes it look as if caring for behaviour is a necessary condition for a claim to care about something to be considered substantial. Indeed, in contexts other than human relationships where, for example, one might talk of caring about the environment or animal rights, it would be considered a misleading and flippant claim if one never did anything that made this claim manifest. As White (1960, p.272) observes: '... we can show care either by doing or not

9

'doing' by which he means that a caring attitude can be made manifest by a refusal to do certain things and a preparedness to do others.

However, any particular claim to care about someone or something is not immediately invalidated by specific lapses in caring for actions. The logic of the relationship between caring about and caring for seems to occur only at the general level, i.e. my particular claim to care about my child is in danger of being invalidated only if lapses to care for are considered by others to be widespread, consistent or of such serious depth (e.g. occasional moments of extreme brutality) that they call into question all the rest of my more benign activities.

Allowing for a conceptually intimate connection at a general level between a claim to care about and caring for actions that are judged to be consistent with it, does not make caring for behaviours either a necessary or sufficient condition for a claim to care about a person to be considered valid (although it still might be the best evidence we have).

I can take care of my tomato plants meticulously and part of this activity will involve a certain sort of attentiveness. I don't forget that the plants need daily watering etc. It would be odd, though, in this context, to infer that therefore I cared about my tomato plants, except in the very minimal sense that I shall be upset if my neighbour's dog tramples all over them and ruins them. This kind of caring about, though, is likely to be prudential in the sense that it merely reflects my interests. I now can't eat the tomatoes I was looking forward to having and I am mindful of all my wasted effort. I could of course care about the destruction of all living things and this would be a moral rather than a prudential view but it would be part of a whole attitude to life which doesn't single out tomatoes in any particular way except in so far as they are living things or God's creation. Similarly, if vandals destroyed the plants while rampaging through my garden, I may care about this very much but part of this concern would have to be understood as a moral response to the behaviour of others: the intrusion and careless disregard of my property or the wanton destruction. It would not be the tomato plants themselves that I would be caring about.

As Philippa Foot (1977) points out, plants, unlike animals perhaps and certainly human beings, have no 'own sakes', so to talk of caring about them as if I could be interested in their flourishing for reasons other than my or other people's economic, nutritive or aesthetic interests would be a strained use of language. Only a religious view of the world could make sense of it, in which case the existence of tomato plants could be seen as expressive of the wonder of God and thus worth preserving but still not for their own sake.

With people and possibly animals (through their shared capacity to feel and suffer) much more substance can be given to the notion of caring about. If, as a good Kantian, I care about you then I am interested in what will be good for you, not for me in relation to you, or not just for this at any rate. Your flourishing is independent of how it might or might not happen to serve my interests (unlike the tomatoes) because I am concerned about you as an end in yourself not merely as a means to an end of mine (O'Neill, 1985). However, rather as with plants people can 'cultivate' each other for all sorts of self interested and sometimes malign purposes that have nothing whatsoever to do with caring about the other person, so it seems clear so far that while caring for in general terms is intimately connected to a claim to care about, it in no way constitutes either a necessary or a sufficient condition for such a claim. The caring for in such a context could be so proficient in a technical sense that the recipient could come to believe that he/she really was cared about and hence the deception would be complete. This might be the sort of deception exercised by pimps to lure young girls into working for them as prostitutes. However, that such a deception usually comes to be seen at some point for what it is, suggests that eventually something in the cared for experience ceases to add up, in the mind of the recipient, to being cared about and the fundamentally exploitative nature of what is going on is revealed.

This rather suggests that for any cared for experience to endure and be considered sincere in human relations it has to be accompanied, at least to some degree, by an attitude of caring about. If this is so then it has some interesting implications for health care. The question arises as to whether or not health care professionals care in an enduring enough way for caring about to be a necessary accompaniment of caring for, or whether the relationship is of such a transitory nature, the caring about dimension never needs to feature. It might of course depend on the context; the rapid turn-over of an accident and emergency department resulting in a very different pattern of care from that of a rehabilitation unit.

Curzer (1993) when talking about care and health care professionals, certainly tries to drive a wedge between the concepts of caring about and caring for. He rightly points out that if health care professionals care too much about their patients this can be both counter-productive for patients (uncomfortable, intrusive familiarity which may not be welcomed) and for staff. In the latter case it is likely to lead to 'burn out' and an inability to maintain the necessary objectivity of a professional person. A nurse graphically describes this difficulty as follows:

'I just could not take care of him. I just felt too bad for him. I just felt so overwhelmed by all these losses, and I felt so bad for his wife, I cried every time I saw her ... When you can't step back far enough not to feel so devastated yourself ... you're one step too close to the patient.' (Ramos, 1992, p.501)

11

According to Curzer all that is necessary for a professional health carer to care effectively for patients is technical ability and a general attitude of benevolence. To this end, he suggests that any inherent dishonesty in the relationship of seeming to care about one's patients when one doesn't is in fact unproblematic and perhaps even a necessary deception. MacIntyre (1975) would probably draw the same conclusion that deception exists, but for him it would have malign rather than benign consequences. With regard to social work he sees the apparent friendliness of the relations a social worker tries to establish with clients as being part of the armoury of the social worker in his/her exercise of power over unsuspecting clients (MacIntyre, 1975, p.106). These are powerful critiques which invite an effective response and will be returned to later.

First, however, it may be easier to examine the relationship of caring about and caring for in a lay context and then to see what of this (if anything) is relevant to the health care context. Could, for instance, a mother care for her child adequately if she didn't care about her child? I think one wants to say, yes up to a point, for on occasions parents may actively dislike their children or there may be a delay in bonding between mother and infant such that the mother feels uninterested in, or even a degree of hostility towards, her baby. At the extreme end, these feelings are likely to lead to a gross failure of care and be expressed via neglect and/or more active forms of abuse. However, such attitudes, depending of course on their degree, do not necessarily mean that there would be any obvious failure to care for the child. Nevertheless, given lengthy exposure to such an environment, one would wonder about the long-term effects on the child's capacity to thrive. This is because human thriving isn't merely dependent on what is necessary for bodily activity and growth. A sense of being loved and cared about seems to matter to infants and people in general. Given a background of mixed experience, it seems reasonable to assume that infants learn quickly to differentiate between sincere and insincere expressions of care because it is in their survival interests to be able to do so.

To make the same point differently, suppose I detest my mother-in-law but, out of a sense of duty, I care for her diligently when she comes to stay. Nourishing meals are served punctually but either she eats alone or there is an undisguisable frostiness at the dining table. What I can't do is be friendly to someone I detest, no matter how hard I try. Either my frostiness or her solitary eating might be enough to make her lose her appetite or develop indigestion because veiled hostility is unlikely to be perfectly veiled. Thus the effectiveness of my caring activities are likely to be diminished despite my best efforts because I simply don't care enough about her. Equally, though, 'caring about' is not in itself enough to ensure that adequate caring practices will take place, for whatever my good will and affection I might be an appalling cook such that the meal is barely edible anyway. A degree of appropriate 'know how' is important.

At this point it could look as if caring about might be interchangeable with liking but on closer inspection this appears not to be so. In my preceding examples, I used the words 'detest' and 'extreme indifference' to indicate complete failures of caring about a person. Where we simply dislike someone, it remains I think, perfectly possible to speak of caring about them, at least to a degree. As an employer, for instance, I might dislike one of my employees but nevertheless maintain a sense of respect for that person such that I would be prepared to assist him or her in pursuit of his or her career and write favourable references to facilitate this. To this extent my caring for gestures would be paralleled by a limited 'caring about' attitude despite my personal dislike. With intense reactions such as hatred however, it is difficult to envisage how a 'caring about' attitude could be said to survive and if one detected it in a friend one would probably challenge the claim to hate by saying: 'But you don't really do you?'

So far then the conclusion is that, at least in a lay context, caring about is a precondition for caring for persons if it is to occur in any sustained way, but this makes it neither a necessary condition (where the relationship between the two is of a logical nature such that it must occur on every occasion) nor a sufficient condition (such that the very presence of the former would alone guarantee the presence of the latter). Similarly, caring for behaviour is the expected manifestation (at least to some degree) of any sincere claim to care about another person. This again is not a strictly logical connection but the concepts are more than just contingently related because over a long period of time the absence of caring for behaviour would result in the claim to care about being questioned. The phrase 'conceptually intimate relationship' is used here to try and capture this not strictly logical but not strictly contingent kind of connection between 'caring for' and 'caring about'.

## Caring and uncaring

'Caring' used as an adjective and its opposite 'uncaring' are clearly morally evaluative descriptions of persons or their actions. Generally speaking it is considered good to be caring and bad to be uncaring and this moral weighting can be taken for granted in conversation. However, we do say of some people that they are too caring and by this we may or may not imply moral criticism. It could for instance be said in a context where someone has given all their money away to a needy relative which, while morally commendable, is not considered wise in the sense of prudent. If, of course, prudence is viewed as a virtue, rather than merely a pragmatic reflection of self interest, moral censure might also be implicit in the phrase 'too caring'. In other contexts though, there will be little ambiguity; moral censure will clearly be meant. Consider, for instance, the mother who maintains such strict supervision of her teenage son that he rarely has to make a decision and virtually never has to take any risks. Such a person could be described as being too caring because such a degree of care may be considered to be positively unkind. It is ill-preparing her son to be able to stand on his own feet in adulthood. The judgement that she is too caring thus reflects moral criticism. However, in such an instance, it wouldn't be in question that the mother cared about her son (although one might want to say that her care was somewhat misguided) nor would it be the case that she didn't care for her son. Nevertheless, one wants to say the care is misdirected and over involved.

One might of course be tempted to add that if she really cared, then this mother would not behave as she does, implying that there is something ignorant or self deceiving about what she is doing, such that the apparent care is not real care at all. She is blind to the real needs of her child. This view turns caring into a virtue such that bad care/caring becomes an incoherent notion. Many nurses seem to be tempted by such a position but this view is open to the kind of objections that Allmark raises. He says with reference to caring that: 'First the person must care about the right things ... second, the person must care in the right way' (Allmark, 1995, p.23). According to Allmark, these judgements cannot be made via an analysis of the concept of care, nor via an analysis of so called caring acts in isolation. One has to introduce other moral values or principles in relation to which the caring behaviour is then evaluated. In the case of the mother, previously described, her too caring attitude is judged in relation to some standard of mothering considered good enough to permit children to flourish and of course such standards may differ from person to person and community to community. She, for instance, may see nothing wrong with what she does and others may agree with her. The onus is on the person who thinks she is too caring to show why he thinks so.

Her failure to care adequately, even if agreed by many including herself, does not however render her necessarily uncaring. She might, for instance impress all around her with her personal courage and commitment in coming to see that her blind spot resulted from a sense of a lack of being cared for in her own right and a wish therefore to keep her child as a carer for herself. Such preparedness to undertake painful self scrutiny could not possibly spring from an uncaring or indifferent attitude towards her child. That we describe her as too caring rather than uncaring is a very precise distinction which would be unintelligible if caring in and of itself was a virtue regardless of the ends it served. One simply cannot be too virtuous except in the sense of too self satisfied.

In order to move on to see what relevance all these considerations have in understanding the nature of professional care, it is of course necessary to look at least at some of the features that both kinds of care share and some features in which they differ. A few distinctions come to mind.

Professional care of any kind has time boundaries. Parenting, on the other hand, is a 24 hour, 365 days per year commitment. Friendships, however, usually do operate within boundaries of time and such conventions are well understood. For example, an invitation to come to dinner is not automatically to be understood as an invitation to stay the night! However, between friends time boundaries will usually be mutually negotiated whereas with professional client/patient care there will be room for only very limited negotiation. If my clinic hours are fixed, I might be prepared to accommodate later or earlier appointments according to patient preference within them. With professional care, remuneration of some kind takes place for the service and what is expected will be specified in a formal or informal contract between the parties themselves or via third parties. Between friends and family members involved in caring for each other, there could be such a contract but there need not be.

Selecting two aspects for comment clearly doesn't exhaust the possibilities of distinguishing between professional and lay care, but it is enough to indicate the emergence of a question. Is it the case that professional care and for the sake of illustration, nursing care, is fundamentally the same as lay care, with any differences being matters of emphasis and questions of degree, or is it the case that they are conceptually distinct? Writers such as Noddings (1984) have made much of the psychological roots of all caring activities and located them with mothers and infants, but while this connection may be important for psychology, it may be philosophically more illuminating to look at possible conceptual distinctions rather than similarities. The argument that the distinction between lay and professional care is merely a matter of emphasis and degree is, however, simpler to pursue and will thus be tackled first.

## A difference of degree?

It would seem clear that the depth of engagement between nurse and patient is likely to be much less than that between parent and child or daughter and elderly parent. The boundaries of time contribute to this but so too does the fact that professional caring is frequently undertaken as a service to strangers. This is likely (but not always) to be quite different from family care which will often be conducted in a context of interpersonal familiarity, if not intimacy. This affects deeply what caring for activities can or can't be done. Precisely because of the familiarity of a relationship some spouses may be quite unable to attend to the physically intimate bodily needs of a suddenly dependent partner and equally the partner, for similar reasons, may be quite unable to receive this care from their spouse (Gilley, 1988). Such care, however, may be tolerable to give and tolerable to receive if it is conducted (initially at least) between strangers. One could conclude that the more distant the persons, the more manageable the shame and embarrassment becomes.

Of course nurses' lack of detailed knowledge about their patients can also have unfortunate consequences in that premature assumptions can be made, resulting in damaging misconstruals of a patient's character and motives; but equally the position of not knowing each other can allow greater freedom for the exploration of particular views and attitudes relating to an illness. Such new views may be important for rehabilitation and they may challenge received family wisdom such as 'Dad can't cook'. Perhaps while his wife was alive, he never needed to try.

The fact that in professional care carers are paid, either directly by the patient or indirectly by the institution, has important consequences for the management of feelings of guilt and indebtedness. If someone is paid to care for me, I presumably feel less obliged to them than I would were such an activity to demand obvious personal sacrifice. Professional care can alleviate much of the guilt of being a burden that anyone dependent on another's care may experience and fear.

So far then the proposition is that a significant difference between professional and lay care is that the former consists initially of an encounter between strangers whereas the latter usually does not. To claim that this is a difference of degree rather than kind, one has to assume that relationships between strangers are at one end of some graded scale of engagement with the most intimate of relationships at the other end. This is an assumption which could be contested and a claim could be made that relationships between strangers are in fact quite different from intimate relationships and to speak of gradations is to introduce an unhelpful quantitative model. Deciding between such perspectives may depend on how one prefers to see it, but a stronger claim can be made for the idea that at least in one respect the distinction between lay and professional care is a difference of kind not of degree. Any such analysis will have to delineate a significant conceptual distiction between professional and lay care irrespective of the areas of overlap and apparent similarity that people such as Noddings have drawn attention to.

## A difference of kind?

Curzer (1993) refers to the balance of emotional attachment and distance that seems to be required of health care professionals (HCPs) to achieve a desirable state of 'detached concern' (Maslach, 1982, pp.147-8). Curzer suggests that these ideas are subject to two possible interpretations, the first being that 'HCPs. should have positive emotional attachment to their patients, but that attachment should be much less than the emotional attachment associated with caring' (Curzer, 1993, p.61). The second interpretation is that 'HCPs should maintain a substantial emotional attachment to their patients, but somehow temper that attachment with detachment' (Curzer, 1993, p.61). Curzer goes on to say that this latter position is unintelligible: 'Like oil and water, detachment and concern do not mix, the recommended attitude is impossible to adopt because detachment and concern are incompatible' (Curzer, 1993, p.62).

It is from this perspective that Curzer then moves to his own position which is close to the first interpretation and which leads him to the somewhat radical conclusion as follows:

> Expecting contemporary H.C.P.'s to care for their patients is as unreasonable as expecting love from a prostitute. In both cases the relationship seems intimate, but the exchange of money, the infrequency of the contact, and the one-dimensionality of the relationship makes the relationship purely professional. Emotional attachment is incidental and destructive to the practice. (Curzer, 1993, p.66)

Curzer is however less radical than this paragraph, taken out of context, might suggest. The strength of his argument depends on splitting the concepts of care and benevolence (Curzer, 1993, p.62). He does not dispute that a benevolent attitude may be necessary for the performance of caring acts but he doesn't view such benevolence as being expressive of caring about the person in question. He suggests that HCPs 'should act as if they are significantly emotionally attached, but in fact should involve their feelings relatively little' (Curzer, 1993, p.62) thereby advocating deception.

To some extent Curzer can of course win his argument by adopting certain definitions, but the question is, is it illuminating or has an oversimplification occurred which masks the real complexity of what takes place between nurse and patient? Previously it was suggested that taking care of people in a lay context is intimately connected conceptually with being able to care about such people despite the fact that the presence of caring behaviour does not ensure the presence of a caring attitude, nor vice versa. Only in general terms must this conceptual relationship exist. However, to provide good nursing care as opposed to something that might pass as rather indifferent care, the connection between caring about and caring for has to become more explicit. This is because although technical ability and a general benevolent disposition towards people may mean one is a technically competent and not unkind nurse, the inspiration required to know what to say and when to say it to capture the moment must, in my view, depend upon some degree of caring about the individual as a particular person. If it isn't timed with great sensitivity, an intervention like the following would simply not work:

> Sue (nurse) described how Naomi (patient) gradually came to accept her amputated stump as part of herself: 'I can remember the first day Naomi massaged her stump. She was so tentative. She was frightened of touching it. So, I just took her through a few basic massage techniques, and said: "It's really nice if you give it a rub like this" ... You could see her during the day: the circles were getting bigger and bigger, and more firm, and the hands and the stump were an item ...'. (Taylor, 1993, p.36)

Where communication is difficult one can see nurses making very deliberate attempts to find out more about the person in order to care for them better. Here an ICU nurse explains why she wants to know about what an unresponsive patient was like before he was sick:

> 'Because it makes me humanize the person or patient more. I treat them more as a human being. I work mostly at night so it is real easy to lose perspective. When I see a patient with glasses on, or a photograph of them, it is so much easier for me to think of them as someone's father or a businessman ... You only lose that as the days go by and you keep the person totally unresponsive, hooked up to the machines ... just a body that you are turning and cleaning, and dressing ...'. (Tanner et al., 1993, p.277)

If the necessity for a relationship between caring about and caring for, for the provision of good nursing care, needs any further demonstration, one can turn to the case of Tony Bland. Tony was a patient in a persistent vegetative state (p.v.s.) and prior to his death, following deliberate withdrawal of treatment (feeding), the chief nurse described how some nurses responded to him: 'Some of the nurses would come in and tell him where they had been the night before, some looked on him as a brother ...' (Alderman, 1993, p.18).

This is, in my view, a clear attempt to construct an identity for and a relationship with a person who, if the diagnosis of p.v.s. was accurate, could neither register the fact of such nursing communications nor respond. My contention is that to continue caring for Tony Bland it was necessary for nurses to construct an identity (based on reports of those who had known him) so that they could care about him and thus care for him well. Where there is any likelihood of recovery, such constructions may be absolutely essential in facilitating it. Where hope seems misplaced, it is likely that nurses will, of all the professional groups involved in care, find it particularly difficult to give up and let go.

18

These illustrations have, I think, clearly demonstrated the importance of the connection between caring about and caring for in the provision of good nursing care and since it makes no sense to speak of insincere caring about, it rather undermines Curzer's (1993) suggestion that a degree of pretence in the relationship between nurse and patient is both inevitable and acceptable. So far however, these ideas illustrate the connection between lay and professional care rather than the distinction. It is now necessary to look at the limits of caring about patients and to consider the question of detachment that Curzer mentions.

In a way that would seem superficially similar to the situation previously described of the too caring mother, nurses can be described as 'over involved' and indeed this is the predicament of the nurse previously quoted who describes herself as being 'too close to the patient' (Ramos, 1992, p.501). However, while in both cases there may be an issue of appropriate distance, the language used also suggests a distinction. It would be odd to describe the mother as too close to her son since it is questionable whether one can be too close to someone one loves; and it would be odd to describe the nurse as too caring because from a nursing perspective it is clear that over-involvement with patients leads to poor or non-existent nursing care. In the lay context, there is some expectation that if the mother agrees with the judgement, she will take a step back and in doing so perhaps come to see that her own needs were interfering with her capacity to care well for her son. This would require her to realign her caring behaviour in accordance with a new view of his needs and her capacity to care about him would thus deepen also. Presumably, his sense of being loved might also increase.

In the professional context, a similar stepping back is required, and perhaps a similar degree of self scrutiny, to try to understand why one has become overinvolved, with the aim of restoring the nursing function in oneself. However such similarity is merely apparent for, unlike the mother-son illustration, in a professional context the patient's ends are only relevant in so far as they concern nursing care and limiting the nature of the relationship between nurse and patient with a view to discharge and separation is as much a proper feature of professional nursing as developing a relationship may be. This limiting feature of the nurse-patient relationship informs its nature from the beginning and makes it quite improper for nurses (unlike parents) to view the maintenance of the relationship as an end in itself.

Against Curzer (1993) I would argue that there can be, indeed often has to be, an oil and water mixture of the elements of attachment and detachment found in professional nursing care. Such a mixture can lead to deception but it need not do so and while difficult to manage and inherently unstable, it can produce a very creative emulsion. One need only perceive it as unintelligible if one has as one's paradigm case for care the lay context, such that professional care is seen to be a pale and distorted shadow of it. For similar reasons, it can be argued that although professional care is sometimes deceptive, it is not intrinsically so. One would only be compelled to take such a view if one considered lay care to be the paradigm where the deepening of the relationship was a proper goal and professional care thus some kind of debasement of this activity, conducted for purposes other than the flourishing of the relationship and the flourishing of the individual lives within the relationship. It is entirely proper for nursing care to have as its purpose patient recovery from (or adjustment to) illness. To this end it is necessary for nurses to find a way of caring about their patients in order to care for them well but the extent of that caring about is properly limited. In itself this makes it neither deceptive nor insincere.

Fortunately for nurses and nursing the 'emulsion state' is often achieved spontaneously and it is only now and again that nurses have to ask of themselves questions such as: 'Am I uncomfortably close to this patient and if so why?' or 'Why can I not seem to get on well enough with this patient to develop a mutual care plan?' The spontaneity is captured well here:

> 'Lillian [patient] returned from the toilet and Sally [nurse] noticed how tall she looked in relation to Lillian. Sally related to Lillian as like her own "wee granny". Sally's remark was said with softness and was received by Lillian as it was intended ...'. (Taylor, 1993, p.37)

Nothing here suggests that there is any deception at work, neither party is confused into really thinking they are grandmother and granddaughter. The 'as if' quality is clearly tender and enhancing of their relationship with its limits accepted. There could of course be pitfalls in that if Lillian were to be mortally ill and if Sally's own grandmother had died, it might be hard for Sally to retain the 'as if' quality and preserve the distance necessary for her to nurse. She might become very upset in a way that would be out of proportion to the depth of her real relationship with Lillian but it wouldn't have to be like this at all. With experience, nurses learn how to preserve the emulsion of engagement and detachment by monitoring both their involvement with and distance from patients.

Parents may sometimes ask similar questions, for example: 'Why aren't we communicating?' asked by a parent of a teenage daughter. Parents may also have metaphorically to take a step back from their customary relationship with their children and reflect upon the different degrees of privacy that children need at different stages in their development, but the standards that parents will use to make these judgements will not be the standards used by a nurse. The nurse does not use some version of a parental standard since any such manoeuvre would be an insult to patients. Instead she uses professional standards, standards that have had to be acquired in the process of learning to nurse.

Nurses can become confused about their role, perceiving patients as friends or family members and doubtless patients can become confused about the proper role of a nurse, but it is part of the nurse's duty to seek help when she becomes confused and to help patients to clarify the situation if they appear confused. If this work is not undertaken rigorously, charges of deception and manipulation could fairly be laid at nursing's door; but in ordinary non-confused contexts, it seems a gross distortion of the nurse-patient relationship and the form of care that expresses it, to perceive it as inherently insincere. For this reason, I reject both MacIntyre's (1975) and Curzer's (1993) respective accusations. Good nursing in any environment of sustained care requires some degree of caring about patients for caring for to take place. A general attitude of benevolence does not capture what nurses in such contexts do, think, feel or say about their relationship with their patients and must therefore be an inadequate description of the attitude necessary to inform good nursing care.

## Bibliography

Alderman, C. (1993), 'A family loss', *Nursing Standard*, Vol. 7, No. 27, 24 March, pp.18-19.

Allmark, P. (1995), 'Can there be an ethics of care?', *Journal of Medical Ethics*, Vol. 21, No. 1, pp.19-24.

Curzer, H.J. (1993), 'Is care a virtue for health care professionals?', *The Journal of Medicine and Philosophy*, 18, pp.51-69.

Foot, P. (1977), 'Euthanasia', *Philosophy and Public Affairs*, Vol. 6, No. 2, Winter, pp.85-110.

Gilley, J. (1988), 'Intimacy and terminal care', *Journal of the Royal College of General Practitioners*, Vol. 38, No. 308, pp.121-2.

MacIntyre, A. (1975), 'How virtues become vices: values, medicine and social context', in Engelhardt H.T. and Spicker, S.F. (eds), *Evaluation and Explanation in the Biomedical Sciences*, D. Reidel Publishing Co., Dordrecht, Holland, pp.97-111.

Maslach, C. (1982), *Burnout: The Cost of Caring*, Prentice Hall, Englewood Cliffs (cited by Curzer).

Noddings, N. (1984), *Caring: A Feminine Approach to Ethics and Moral Education*, University of California Press, Berkeley.

O'Neill, O. (1985), 'Between consenting adults', *Philosophy and Public Affairs*, Vol. 14, No. 3, pp.252-77.

Ramos, M.C. (1992), 'The nurse-patient relationship: theme and variations', *Journal of Advanced Nursing*, 17, pp.496-506.

Tanner, C.A., Benner, P., Chesla, C. and Gordon, D.R. (1993), 'The phenomenology of knowing the patient', *Image: Journal of Nursing Scholarship*, Vol. 25, No. 4, pp.273-80.

Taylor, B. (1993), 'Ordinariness in nursing: a study (part 1)', *Nursing Standard*, Vol. 7, No. 39, 16 June, pp.35-8.

White, A.R. (1960), 'The concept of care', *The Philosophical Quarterly*, Vol. 10, No. 40, pp.271-4.

# 2 Some ideas of the person

*Martyn Evans*

Passing moral judgement on other people's behaviour often seems easy enough in private, but it is considerably less so in print, and on matters that will affect public policy. Making moral decisions regarding our own behaviour is similarly uncomfortable when that behaviour will be watched by others. Hardly anywhere is either of these generalisations more true than in clinical medicine, nor at any time more true than today when medical technology has placed in our hands the care of human beings who until recently could not have remained alive (such as the grossly brain-damaged) and in some cases could not even have been isolated and presented to our gaze (such as the early human embryo). The discomfort of deciding how to treat these unfamiliar human beings is a moral discomfort, and it has both private and public dimensions.

Less uncomfortable than making moral judgements, over which people perennially disagree in peculiarly raw and intensely-felt ways, is the business of scientific classification; that is, of sorting the world out into usable and measurable categories. Scientific classification has broad traditions of agreement that can be used as a basis for new decisions: disagreements here are mostly professional rather than personal matters, and parties to them can usually hope for some new findings or discoveries that will make one side or other conclusively the stronger. Still more reassuring even than the pursuit of orderly classification is the answering of factual questions; these have right and wrong answers that people can't finally dispute, and concerning which it is possible for them to feel on safe ground. So it is perhaps not surprising that, when confronted by unfamiliar kinds of human patient and by the moral challenge of deciding how they ought to be treated, some have looked for the relative security of picking out a special classification into which these patients should be put, and for items of evidence according to which the membership requirements of a particular classification can factually be said to have been met. Thus some writers have picked out a class of patients who are to be called persons and have spelled out the characteristics which any given patient must have if he is to count as a person. By offering a quasi-scientific classification, and by showing how we obtain relevant factual evidence in a particular case, these writers perhaps hope to avoid what they think would otherwise be unsupported, straightforwardly *moral* judgements about how certain sorts of patients should be treated. They hope instead that moral judgements about these patients' treatment will follow as conclusions from their own, less subjective or otherwise suspect, method. I do not share their hope; moreover I think it dangerous.

If discussions in health care ethics or in philosophy of medicine are to remain relevant to practical clinical realities, then they should not lose touch with the everyday, commonsense understandings of the terms that those realities involve. Equally, if philosophical questions, like 'What is a person?' sound strange outside such discussions, then that strangeness ought to be recognised, and we ought be aware of when our abstract reasoning departs to any great distance from ordinary usage in everyday language. The most important reason for this, in my opinion, is that moral discussion about the practice of health care belongs to everyone – practitioners, patients, academics and laymen. Those who debate publicly in health care ethics are sometimes mistakenly thought to have special authority to pronounce on moral matters. In the process of such debate unfamiliar concepts or, more dangerously, unfamiliar interpretations of ordinary concepts, may gain an influence which they do not deserve – partly because of the mystique and authority which is attracted by any idea that sounds technical. I suggest that this has happened with the idea of 'personhood', or 'the person'. I suggest that this is an ordinary idea from ordinary language, which has been given the status of a technical term, and subsequently used by some as though it could settle moral questions in an objective, pseudo-scientific way. The concept of the person is widely thought to be a central idea in any general study of health care ethics, so it is clearly important and influential. I think such influence can be harmful, and I will try to defend this rather uncomfortable suggestion in my conclusion.

When I informally asked a few friends and colleagues *outside* health care ethics what they understood by the idea of a person, they provided some striking answers. A classical philosopher said, 'Someone with a soul'. (Well, of course...) A secretary said, 'A human being', as did a computer programmer. A professor of Italian said, rather intriguingly, 'A human being of any sex'. When pressed, he also added that such a human being ought to have 'rationality or a sense of humour', and he then admitted to having a Scholastic training. A professor of Law also began by saying 'A human being', but when pressed she too added some qualifications: 'My idea of a human being doesn't include a foetus, because I think "human being" means "independent being"'. And another secretary gave a striking, although slightly indirect answer. She said, 'Being a person means being someone in your own right'. (Inevitably, only the classical philosopher took my question as being routine and in need of no explanation.)

Of course informal soundings like this are not research. But at least they invite the thought that there is some variety in the way in which people use the idea of 'the person'; that this variety includes an *unreflective* sense of equivalence between a person and an individual human being as in when we say, 'There were some people in the park taking their dogs for a walk'; and that some then go further, and try to specify the category more closely, in terms of *attainments or capacities*, such as independence, identity, rationality and so on. Most of the various definitions of the person, which are abundant in the literature within philosophical medical ethics, incorporate attainments or capacities in this way. Their credibility rests on whether there is, or can be, any substantial agreement on exactly which attainments or capacities these should be. The implications of a lack of agreement here are crucial, among them that definitions referring to different sets of capacities will have different *exclusions*. Any definition of 'personhood' that is narrower than simply 'individual human being' will rule out some individual human being or other, and, some overlap notwithstanding, different definitions will rule out different individuals. With these exclusions in mind, the following selection of generally recent definitions of 'the person' seems to me instructive:

1  'The person' as value-free description (at least, initially)

It seems advisable to treat the term 'person' as a purely descriptive term, rather than as one whose definition involves moral concepts. For this appears to be the way the term 'person' is ordinarily construed. Second, however, it seems desirable that the descriptive content assigned to the term 'person' be guided by moral considerations, in order to have a term that can play a certain, very important role in the discussion of moral issues. (Tooley, 1983, p. 51)

2  Personhood as a sign of being valuable

I shall use the term person to stand for any being who has what it takes to be valuable ... whatever else they are like. Although in normal use 'person' is just another (and usefully gender-neutral) term for 'human being', as I shall use it from now on it will also be species-neutral as well.
    ... we will have sketched a concept of the person, and of what makes such creatures valuable, which we can apply to the dilemmas which face

25

us every day... . (Harris, 1985, pp.9-10)

## 3 Personhood as the chance of *feeling* valuable

On the account that has emerged, a person will be any being capable of valuing its own existence. ... To kill a person not only frustrates their wishes for their own futures, but frustrates every wish a person has. Creatures that cannot value their own existence cannot be wronged in this way, for their death deprives them of nothing that they can value.

The idea that persons are beings capable of valuing their own existence also gives us a way, at least in principle, of recognising persons when we confront them, although in particular cases this may be no easy matter. (Harris, 1985, pp.9-10)

## 4 Personhood as cognitive capacity

... Aristotle claimed that man is essentially a rational and social animal; Descartes, that thinking is essential to the nature of a person; Locke, that a person is an object essentially aware of its progress and persistence through time; Hume, that persons are bundles of psychological characteristics; Kant, that persons are rational agents who, among other things, can synthesise experience and act on moral principles; and Sartre, that persons are self-conscious, intentional beings.

... what all these philosophers have in common is the belief that some type of cognitive function is necessary for something to be a person. Any being devoid of the capacity for cognitive function would by implication lack each of the particular characteristics that these philosophers use to define persons. (Lizza, 1993, p.355)

## 5 Personhood as cognitive and affective capacity

A human being is a person to the extent that they are a rational self conscious agent with the capacity for the distinctive human emotions and affective ties. So there are some humans who are not persons. (Carruthers, 1989, p.234)

## 6 Personhood as moral wholeness

Note that ... a psychopath – an 'inhuman monster' – is quite literally less of a person than the rest of us. (Carruthers, 1989, p.234)

## 7 Personhood as possession of neurological structures

Although the [President's] Commission did not specifically discuss anencephalics, its conclusion implies that they are living persons. Although anencephalics lack a functional cortex, they have lower-brain-stem functions and therefore are persons. Under the higher-brain formulations, however, anencephalics would not be considered persons, since they have no capacity for cognitive functions. (Lizza, 1993, p.352)

8   Personhood as really useful, or, as the benefit of the doubt

... it is difficult to determine specifically when in human ontogeny persons strictly emerge. Socializing infants into the role *person* draws the line conservatively. Humans do not become persons strictly until some time after birth. ...This ascription of the role *person* constitutes a social practice that allows the rights of a person to be imputed to forms of human life that can engage in at least a minimum of social interaction. The interest is in guarding anything that could reasonably play the role *person* and thus to strengthen the social position of persons generally. (Engelhardt, 1982, p.97)

... It should be stressed that the social sense of person is primarily a utilitarian construct. A person in this sense is not a person strictly, and hence not an unqualified object of respect. Rather, one treats certain instances of human life as persons for the good of those individuals who are persons strictly. As a consequence, exactly where one draws the line between persons in the social sense and merely human biological life is not crucial as long as the integrity of persons strictly is preserved. Thus there is a somewhat arbitrary quality about the distinction between fetuses and infants. ... One might retort, Why not include fetuses as persons in a social sense? The answer is, Only if there are good reasons to do so in terms of utility. (Engelhardt, 1982, p.98)

9   Personhood as the ground of conscious identity

Those who deny the personhood of the human embryo typically reduce the person to personal consciousness, and they argue that, since there is no personal consciousness in the embryo, there can be no person. Their inference is irresistible if they are right in reducing the person to personal consciousness. I will try to show that they are not right, and will try to do this by bringing out the distinction between *being* and *consciousness* in ourselves as persons. I will try to show that as persons we are not all consciousness, or all self-consciousness, or self-presence, or conscious acting and experiencing, but that we have a personal being which has to be distinguished from personal consciousness, which can even exist apart from consciousness. Then I will try to determine the assumptions which,

27

given this distinction, we have to make about the status of the human embryo. (Crosby, 1993, p.400)

10 Personhood as individual humanity

...the accepted criterion for being considered a person ...[is] live birth of the product of a human conception. (Capron, 1987, p.10)

11 Personhood as the possibility of consciousness

Consciousness, a necessary condition for psychological continuity, is the sine qua non of personal existence. Since upper-brain death results in the permanent absence of consciousness, it is the death of the person ... upper-brain death generates at best a vegetative, not a personal, existence; a person in such a situation is dead. (Gervaise, 1986, p.157)

12 Personhood as conscious mental life

... [T]he justification for an upper-brain-death criterion would be better enunciated thus: the individual's essence consists in the possession of a conscious, yet not necessarily continuous, mental life; if all mental life ceases, the person ceases to exist; when the person ceases to exist, the person has died. Upper-brain death destroys all the capacity for a conscious mental life, and it is therefore the death of the person. (Gervaise, 1986, pp.157-8)

13 Personhood as metaphysical, first and foremost

... we should use moral considerations not as the basis for our analysis but as a guide in framing that analysis so that it will be maximally useful in resolving the conceptual problem at hand. ... we commonly and most easily defend conclusions about moral personhood by appeal to features of metaphysical personhood. ... Ontological analysis is the most suitable philosophical tool for examining our notion of the death of a person. My analysis helps us specify the conditions under which a person ceases to exist, and as a result we can see that the onset of permanent unconsciousness is a person's death. (Gervaise, 1986, p.181)

Between them, these various definitions rule out anencephalic newborns, newborns generally, the comatose, those in the persistent vegetative state, foetuses and, on one account, anyone at all who is incapable of valuing his own existence. On the other hand none of these various unfortunate individuals is ruled out by *all* the definitions - hence to the extent that their exclusions differ, these definitions are in conflict with each other. Since we cannot find any general agreement on what is the proper definition of the concept 'person' or 'personhood', whose definition ought we to accept, and how could we decide the matter?

To approach these two rather large questions, we must first ask what sort of prior question it is which evidently underlies them: namely, the question, 'What is a person?'. For instance, is this an *empirical* question, that could be settled by discovering the relevant facts? We don't need to reflect on this for very long before we can be quite certain that the question, 'What is a person?', is not an empirical or factual question. No amount of research using clipboards, tape-recorders, butterfly nets, microscopes or chemical retorts is going to settle it for us. The reason for this is obvious: factual discoveries in this sense are confined to discovering whether a particular specimen has, or has not, certain definite and describable features – such as whether a given human individual has been born, has a developed forebrain, has the capacity for reason, has developed the ability to value his own existence, and has so far managed to avoid serious head injury. These are, with certain minor difficulties, questions that can be settled by any competent researcher. Of course, these matters are not the problem which faces us. Our problem is to decide which of these definite features ought to count as relevant empirical evidence. And that is not itself a further empirical matter at all.

So if the problem is not an empirical one, then perhaps it is what most people take it to be, namely a *conceptual* or alternatively theoretical question. That is to say, the problem is one of deciding, if we can, which abstract and general account best describes or explains the concrete particular phenomena in which we are interested. This looks to be a more promising solution, and one which would enjoy the support of many scholars. Unfortunately, I think that this will give us only an incomplete picture of the sort of disagreement which is going on.

The reason for this is to do with why different concepts of the person are formulated. They do not arise in a vacuum; they arise because someone has a need for a definition that can be applied to a particular problem. This I believe has generally been the case in mainstream philosophy, from where – perhaps – health care ethics has borrowed the question, 'What is a person?'. It is true that in the twentieth century the philosophical problem has often been primarily an intellectual one in its own right, pursued above all because it was interesting, or because it offered a perspective on other interesting intellectual problems in the philosophy of mind, such as the problem of personal identity. However elsewhere in the history of philosophy I think we can say that the question has more often been a somewhat practical one. The problem might be that of discovering whether we can legitimately make a distinction between the treatment of human beings and the treatment of other animals whom we kill for food, clothing and other products. Or it might be the problem of describing the place of humankind in the Divine order, and of accounting for – or even justifying – the belief that Man is made in the image of God, when most of the evidence seems to point in the other direction. Arguably the most significant role for the concept of the person in traditional philosophy lies in the work of Locke and Kant, who each wished to define the characteristics of a moral *agent*, that is to say an individual who could properly carry moral responsibility for what she thought, said and did.

This concern with practical purposes has, I want to suggest, become intensified in the disciplines of philosophy of medicine and health care ethics. However, here our questions invariably concern what we can or must do to other people. Accordingly in these disciplines, the intended role of the concept of personhood is to help us to identify the characteristics of a moral *subject* rather than a moral agent, and more particularly the characteristics of a moral subject who is to enjoy moral and legal protections to the full. And the practical purposes at stake here are obvious: Which patients must we continue to treat? Which patients may be allowed to die or, in the case of the foetus, be put to death? On whom may we conduct lethal research? From whom may we take tissues or organs without direct consent to do so? The practical importance and urgency of these questions is obvious, and so is their moral character: that is, in asking them we are obviously asking explicitly moral questions. My claim is that these moral questions are so embedded in the search for a definition of 'the person' that the apparently conceptual nature of any disagreement about the concept is incomplete and provisional. At the root of the conceptual disagreement is a *moral disagreement* about how in fact different individuals ought to be treated.

Now someone might object to this by suggesting that I have put matters the wrong way round – that it is not until we are clear what *sort* of individual we are talking about that we can know how she should be treated. This makes it look as if we could, coolly and from a position of morally-neutral detachment, reflect on what characteristics ought to be held by any individual in order for them to have the full status of moral subject. This then amounts to a consideration of what features or characteristics are morally significant. Now of course people can and do reflect on this, and they do and – so far as I can see – always will disagree about their choice of characteristics. But it should immediately be obvious that someone who thinks that (for example) rationality has more moral significance than (for example) species membership is making a *moral choice*, is taking a moral view. What morally neutral position is this? None at all. Please note that I am not saying that that particular view is a bad view (though I suspect it may be); I am merely saying it is not a morally-neutral view.

But someone might further object, and say that I have misrepresented the sort of reasoning in which they are engaged. They might try to deny that they are engaged in an act of choosing morally significant characteristics, and they might try to claim instead that they are merely *analysing* or unpacking the ordinary concept 'person', and telling us what they have discovered. As such the process of definition, they might claim, is transparent to any moral weight the concept itself already has, and they are not responsible for any moral implications which the definition might carry. But this objection is pretty implausible, for a very good reason: namely, that it utterly fails to explain why there could be persistent disagreement about the narrower, technical concept of 'the person'. If a single and determinate meaning were there to be uncovered, then it should surely have been uncovered long ago, and the single agreed definition would be available to all, free from controversy. Moreover if this were true and a single agreed definition were in current use, then philosophy must be an extraordinarily inept discipline conducted by the least competent users of ordinary language, marked out by their inability to notice what everyone else has always known. However, there is something uncomfortable about this reflection, and we might suggest that questions which make sense *within* a discipline can appear slightly crazy to those outside it. And indeed in ordinary non-technical usage I think 'person' just does mean 'individual human being', no more no less. I will come back to this in my conclusion.

At any rate, this ordinary concept can give no comfort to the present objection; for it is within daily clinical practice, and not within academic philosophy, that the question arises of which individuals we ought to treat. And if there really is a *philosophically* bullet-proof single definition of the concept 'person', then either ordinary language users haven't heard of it or, if they have, they have discovered that it isn't any use in settling their moral problems, despite the best hopes of writers in the field. Indeed I am persuaded that this is exactly how things stand: definitions of the concept of the person *are* no use in settling moral questions about whom we ought to treat, and how we ought to treat them. What's more, I think this failure is both obvious and inevitable.

There are two ways of expressing the failure, and I think that between them they are comprehensive. Either there is indeed a definitive morally neutral understanding of the concept of the person; in this case, since moral disagreements are persistent, applying the definitive concept of the person has evidently left the moral problems untouched. (This is hardly surprising, since no genuinely morally-neutral starting point is ever going to generate substantial moral conclusions.) Or alternatively (and to my mind more plausibly) the narrow, technical conceptions of the person are morally-loaded after all. However, this means among other things that they cannot be definitive, and that in putting forward different definitions of the concept, people are ultimately putting forward substantially different moral views.

31

This seems to me to be overwhelmingly the best explanation for why, even within philosophy of medicine and health care ethics, there is continuing disagreement over the concept of the person, and a glance at the selection of writings we considered above shows that they constitute substantial moral positions. At least some of the authors in question, most obviously perhaps Harris and Engelhardt, are well aware of this and indeed rightly insist upon it. So I think we now have the answers to the two large questions which confronted us: first, it is highly unlikely that there will ever be general agreement on the question of which capacities or attainments should go into the definition of the person, since it is highly unlikely that we will ever find general agreement in our responses to the great moral challenges of clinical practice. We can look for it, we can debate about it, but we shouldn't be surprised if we don't find it. Second, there is no independent or morally neutral route to deciding whose definition of the concept 'person' is the one we ought to accept, since ultimately the question itself is not independent of the particular moral views that different people hold.

Since I said earlier that in ordinary usage, 'person' just means 'individual human being', no more, no less, it might seem that at least this ordinary usage *does* amount to a determinate, descriptive definition of the concept of the 'person'. However it is clearly not the one that people are searching for in debates within health care ethics or philosophy of medicine, and it is perfectly obvious why: people are looking for a criterion for *discriminating among* individual human beings, hoping thereby to be able to decide which ones not to treat, which ones to do experiments on and so forth. Only a narrower criterion can choose among individual human beings, and we have seen that several different versions of a narrower criterion are available to choose from.

But what do we think we have got when we have chosen one? One thing we have certainly *not* got is a familiar notion from ordinary language. However there is obviously a temptation to treat the two notions as similar in at least one respect: virtually everyone recognises that statements like 'There are people in there!' carry a serious moral weight if they are spoken in the right circumstances – for instance, in front of a building which is on fire. That is, everyone knows that even the ordinary notion of a person is a morally significant one. If we introduce a narrower notion of 'the person' into the moral challenges of clinical practice, nobody would doubt that this narrower notion carries the same sort of moral weight as the familiar one. After all that is its whole point: to give us a criterion for picking out moral subjects. But of course, these narrower notions typically, and intentionally, exclude different individual human beings who would be *included* under the familiar, ordinary language notion.

Imagine, for instance, that there is a fire in an Intensive Therapy Unit, and someone says, 'Get those people out of there!'. In ordinary language that means, 'Get all the patients out and everyone else who is in the unit'. If someone said, instead, 'Get all the persons out of there!', then on some of the definitions which have seriously been put forward, the question now arises as to whether it is really necessary to save every individual patient from the flames – at least, whether doing that is necessary in order to obey the instruction. Perhaps we would still get all the patients out, and make the distinctions between the different senses of 'person' only later, when things had calmed down. But that is to evade the implications of the narrower notions of 'person': they aim at showing what we ought to do when it really matters, no matter how much of a hurry we might be in. Again, it's true that questions about the allocation of life-saving resources *can* be addressed in a slightly less hurried way. Does that mean that the narrower notion of 'the person' can be applied coolly, without the possibility of confusion, and without incurring moral harm?

Those who propose these narrower definitions must answer 'Yes' to this question, I think. Of course they are entitled to their own moral point of view, and sceptics like me can do no more than disagree with them when the question is put in clearly moral terms. But I am worried that these proposals may be mistaken for something else – for scientific criteria that can be applied in a morally-neutral way.

Someone might now finally object: but of course, we could have a hundred reasons for wanting to save every patient from the fire, whether or not they should be regarded as persons in the narrower sense. My reply is that those other reasons are in danger of being overlooked and finally forgotten. And this danger arises precisely from the equivocation between the familiar and the narrower, technical sense of 'person'. For instance, consider this further definition of 'the person':

> ... whatever one's concept of a person is, one feature widely acknowledged as *necessary* for being a person is a capacity – or at least the potential for a capacity – for consciousness. It follows that when a person has permanently lost the capacity for consciousness – as occurs in brain death – the person no longer exists; the person is dead. (Gillon, 1990, p.4)

Well, capacity for consciousness can permanently be lost without one's being brain dead, and the debate about so-called neocortical death took place on precisely this ground. *Does* it really follow, as Gillon claims, that because it is 'widely acknowledged' within a professional debate that we should pay special attention to the capacity for consciousness, then we can say of the permanently comatose that 'The person is dead'? And if someone does say it, for instance in a public announcement made by a hospital spokesman, should we expect people in general to understand that 'the person' here refers to a narrow, technical conception rather than the familiar notion from ordinary daily usage? Can we be confident that we or they will always know which sense is intended, if the speaker forgets to tell us? We should ask ourselves how easy it might become to think we were speaking of one idea when we were really speaking about another; how easy it might be, perhaps, to apply the narrower concept of the person and somehow not notice, after a while or after getting used to it, how we were *automatically* excluding some individual human beings from the moral respect which we would ordinarily give them. It is this automatic move that worries me, for what we are doing is replacing a moral response to a moral challenge with a sort of technical judgement. We are replacing the moral question instead of facing it.

Routine clinical practice requires doctors to take many kinds of moral decision, and to accept the responsibility for doing so. Like the rest of us, doctors can be forgiven for disliking the responsibility for moral decisions. As trained scientists, many doctors have a natural preference for the fixed, ready-to-apply criteria of the physical sciences, where there are, they suppose, right and wrong answers about which no-one can disagree. I think that if we look at the recent debates over so-called medical futility, over destructive research on early human embryos, over the definitions of brain death and over proposals for a neocortical understanding of human life and death, we can clearly see the belief that our moral problems (concerning how we ought to treat particular people) could somehow be replaced with much more comfortable *technical* or *methodological* questions, questions that have correct and incorrect answers. In all of these examples, appeals to narrower definitions of the concept of the person play a central role in the proposals for technical solutions to moral problems. Doctors are trained in diagnosis, and it is understandable that some doctors would prefer making diagnoses to making moral choices. But the respect owed to the moral subject who is the patient in front of us cannot be dicovered by diagnosis or by using technical criteria, because neither the category of the person, nor the moral status of people, is a technical notion. It is dangerous for doctors to believe otherwise, and, I would say, dangerous if professional philosophers encourage them to believe it.

### Acknowledgement

I am grateful to Richard Bryden, Neil Pickering and Hugh Upton for comments on drafts on this discussion, and to Henk ten Have and colleagues at the European Bioethics Seminar, Nijmegen, the Netherlands, for the invitation to present it in an earlier form and for comments on that presentation.

## Bibliography

Capron, A. (1987), 'Anencephalic donors: separate the dead from the dying', *Hastings Center Report*, Vol. 17, No. 1, pp.5-9.

Carruthers, P. (1989), *Introducing Persons*, Routledge, London.

Crosby, J.F. (1993), 'The personhood of the human embryo', *Journal of Medicine and Philosophy*, Vol. 18, No. 4, pp.399-417.

Engelhardt, H.T. (1982), 'Concepts of personhood', in Beauchamp, T.L. and Walters, L. (eds), *Contemporary Issues in Bioethics*, 1st edition, Wadsworth, Belmont, California, pp.94-101.

Gervaise, K.G. (1986), *Redefining Death*, Yale University Press, Yale.

Gillon, R. (1990), 'Death', (editorial), *Journal of Medical Ethics*, Vol. 16, No. 1, pp.3-4.

Harris, J. (1985), *The Value of Life*, Routledge, London.

Lizza, J. (1993), 'Persons and Death', *Journal of Medicine and Philosophy*, Vol. 18, No. 4, pp.351-374.

Tooley, M. (1983), *Abortion and Infanticide*, Clarendon Press, Oxford.

# 3 The debate on abortion

Zbigniew Szawarski

Abortion is usually performed for one of three reasons: because of a threat to the life or health of the mother; for the good of the foetus; or for so-called social reasons. The dynamic development of medicine and medical prevention has resulted in a situation where pregnancy rarely poses a substantial threat to the mother's life or health. Abortion is still performed, however, for genetic and social reasons. In speaking about social reasons, I refer to all those factors which a woman or the law consider as justifying abortion, and which cannot be reduced to the genetic or medical. Thus, it does not matter whether we speak about family and career planning, rape, or poor living conditions and the alcoholism of the husband. All these are 'social reasons' in the proposed broad sense of the word. Still, whatever the reason that determines the decision to carry out abortion, it may not be enough to justify it morally.

Contemporary ethical literature distinguishes between three fundamentally different approaches towards abortion. The traditional approach, characteristic of the moral doctrine of the Catholic Church, unequivocally states that the foetus is an innocent human being (person) from the moment of conception, therefore each abortion is murder of an innocent person, and as such is a crime and should be banned by law. The liberal approach usually ignores the moral status of the foetus, treating it as tissue, part of the mother's body, or sometimes even as an independent human organism, but one without any relevant moral properties, or one whose moral properties are not important enough to determine the woman's decision concerning the planning of her own life. For a woman may have children if she decides to have them, but she has no moral obligation whatsoever to have a child if the pregnancy, for example, resulted from a rape, if it is due to the unreliability of contraceptives, or to any other reasons that threaten the woman's autonomy, or her right to make decisions concerning herself. This approach is popular among western feminist movements, as it contends that a woman's right to decide about her body overrides the possible right of the foetus to live. The moderate approach embraces a great number of variable ideas whose common feature is the belief that becoming a human being is a process, and that at certain stages of this process an embryo is certainly not a human being or a person, whereas at other stages it certainly is human and should be protected by law and morality. It is a matter of dispute when this transformation takes place. Some assume that this moment coincides with the implantation of the zygote in the uterus, some others choose the emergence of the brain and sufficiently developed nervous system; others point to the moment of quickening, viability or even birth. Whatever the choice of general approach, or more specific solution within that approach, the standard argument against abortion may be presented in the form of the following syllogism: 'The killing of a human being (person) is always wrong; the foetus is a human being (person); therefore, the killing of the foetus is always wrong'. If we leave aside the major premise of that reasoning there are three particular questions which usually arise in most debates about abortion: (1) What begins at the moment of conception? (2) What is a person? and (3) Is it possible to reach a consensus on the abortion issue?

## What begins at the moment of conception?

At the moment of conception, two gametes, the male and the female, join and create a fertilised egg, or zygote. A new organism is produced this way, and from this moment on it will develop according to its specific genetic programme, until it reaches full maturity and then starts slowly to decline. The moment of conception is thus the mere beginning of a certain biological process which is subject to specific biological laws. And it is at this point that hard facts end, and the quagmire of philosophical inquiries and interpretations begins.

For to say that a new organism appears at the moment of conception is a trivial statement which applies equally to all species that reproduce through sexual intercourse. A human life begins the same way as the life of a rabbit or a rat. For what reason, then, is the problem of abortion raised exclusively with regard to the human species, while nobody ever seriously considered it in the case of other mammals? The answer to this question, some people think, is simple: if an entity is a human organism, a human life, a human being, or a human person, than it has an absolute value and should never be destroyed, other things being equal. Some philosophers will see no difference at all between these concepts, some others will try to distinguish carefully between, e.g., 'a human being' meaning 'being a member of the species of *homo sapiens*' and 'being a human person'. Fortunately, we do not need to enter into that subtle argument at this point, because what is most important is the question: what does it mean *to be human* at all? Is it a statement of fact only ('No doubt; it *is human* DNA') or is it a statement of value ('You cannot experiment with it: It *is* a *human* embryo')? Can we offer a morally neutral definition of being human?

Let us assume that at the moment of conception a new human organism, a new human life appears. But this does not mean that a fertilised human egg cell suddenly acquires a particular human aura ('humanness', 'personhood') which makes it absolutely valuable. The statement 'It is a human zygote' does not mean the same as the statement 'It is a human person'. The acorn, one famous argument holds, is not identical with the fully grown oak. At the moment of conception, indeed, a new organism emerges, a new life, and nothing more than that. Even if it is a human life, this fact by itself and without any additional value assumptions is not sufficient to establish that a human life has a value precisely because it is a human life. How absurd an analogous argument would sound: 'a rabbit's life has an absolute value simply because it is rabbit's life'. There is no 'rabbithood' distinctive to its species which makes the rabbit's life sacred.

Still, the matter is neither so simple nor so obvious. I was trying to distinguish and contrast a purely descriptive and a purely prescriptive meaning of 'to be human'. One might argue, however, that it is exactly being human that constitutes a certain unique blend of facts and values, namely the one in which a statement of fact would be indistinguishable from a statement of value. This is the kind of argument typical of the Catholic doctrine of abortion. If human life is a process, which is an evident truth, and if a certain property can be attributed to any phase of this process, then the same property can be attributed to the beginning of this process. Since I am human now, I was human at the moment of my birth, as well as a day (week, month etc.) before my birth, and therefore I am human from the moment of my conception.

It is not difficult to point out the suspicious character of such reasoning. Let us assume that somebody is completely bald now. It does not at all mean that this person was bald twenty years ago, at the moment of his birth, or immediately after conception. Thus, since it is an obvious absurdity to say 'This zygote is bald', is not the statement 'This zygote is human' equally absurd? One could reply to this that the predicates 'to be bald' and 'to be human' belong to different logical categories. Using a certain philosophical language we can say that being bald is an accidental characteristic, while being human is an essential characteristic, an attribute. One *is* or *is not* human, whereas one may *become* bald. The point is, however, that in one sense 'to be human' is indeed a structural property (an attribute), and in another sense it is a developmental one. So we can legitimately say both that one is or is not human, and one is more or less human or is simply becoming or ceasing to be human. How this is possible is evident if we realise that 'to be human' has at least two radically different meanings: (1) to have certain descriptive properties specific to the species of *homo sapiens* (e.g. human DNA, human blood, a human body, a human face); (2) to have certain descriptive value-making properties.

In the first meaning the 'being human' is indeed a structural property because human DNA is present in the human gametes and at the moment of conception a new human life, a new human organism, or a new genetic human structure emerges. In the second meaning 'being human' is a developmental property, because it is a question of time when a human organism acquires that relevant characteristic (or set of them) which makes it valuable. It is of course possible to argue that it is precisely human DNA which is a primary value-making characteristic and it is precisely our genetic endowment which makes human life so valuable, but then we are coming back to the rabbit argument. We identify or infer statements of value from statements of facts. I am not arguing here that the human genetic structure should never be treated as a value-making property. I am saying only that if we treat it this way we are changing the meaning of 'being human' from a purely descriptive to a strongly evaluative one. If there is a class of value-making properties of being human, then our genetic structure is certainly a value-making property, but it is not the only property and it is doubtful even that it the most important one. We can always say that though it is a necessary condition of being human, it is certainly not a sufficient one. Thus at the moment of conception we begin our biological entering into the species of *homo sapiens*, but the biology itself is not enough to give an absolute value to our existence. Whatever our definition of being human is, then, it will always contain some moral substance as it will be a result of a moral choice between different options, different criteria, and different ideals of our humanity.

### Who is a person?

It might be said that it is not a proper thing to equate a human organism to a rabbit organism, or to compare the property of 'being human' to 'being bald'. If there is anything which distinguishes the human organism among the class of all living organisms it is the fact that it has human potential; that it is, or will in a certain period of time, become a person, while a rabbit will

40

never live a personal life. The force of this argument depends on the understanding of the concept of the person. We cannot decide if a zygote is an actual or potential person until we know exactly how to recognise a human person. Of course we can ask a philosopher for some help but probably the best advice we can get is the following: there are so many different concepts of person that it is impossible to suggest any universally accepted and adequate definition of it. Whatever the definition we choose, we will always have to pay some moral price for it. Let us choose, for example, one of the recent interpretations of the concept of a person, to see what the consequences are of that concept for the abortion debate.

Daniel Dennett (1981, pp.269-71) says that if something is to be called a person:

1  It must be a rational being.

2  It must be a being to which certain psychological or mental predicates can be attributed such as: [he] 'thinks, feels, desires, intends, plans, etc'.

3  It must be a being toward which we take some attitude, treating it in a special way, such that this is in part constitutive of its being a person.

4  It must be a being capable of reciprocating that personal attitude in some way.

5  It must be a being capable of verbal communication.

6  It must be a being equipped with a special kind of consciousness which might be called self-consciousness.

If these are indeed the necessary conditions for being a person, then not only zygotes, foetuses, and infants are not persons, but also some adults who, for instance, suffer deep and irreversible brain injuries, are not persons either. For is it possible to ascribe to a zygote the ability to think? Does somebody who has totally lost his ability to communicate with the world as a result of deep and irreversible damage to his brain, satisfy the above conditions? On the other hand, however, if we assume a weaker interpretation of Dennett's conditions, if we recognise that it is sufficient to satisfy only one or a few criteria in order to be considered a person, then it will turn out that we will have to treat a computer as a person if it is capable of entering into a rational dialogue. We will also have to treat at least some animals as persons (if they think, make plans, and perhaps are even capable of showing gratitude, not to mention a disposition to evoke in us a special personal attitude: 'You know,

Rex is a real member of our family'). But does that mean that they are really persons like us?

Suppose, however, that a given being must satisfy all the six criteria in order to be considered a person. Then there arises a fundamental question whether all these criteria must be satisfied at the same time and to the same extent. It could seem - and such is the traditional interpretation - that 'being a person' is a structural property: one either is, or is not a person, but one certainly cannot be a person to a greater or lesser extent. On the other hand, if we consider Dennett's criteria it becomes evident that a person is defined in terms of developmental properties. One can be more or less rational or intelligent; one can be more or less capable of sensual experience of the world. One can use a language better or worse. What, however, if one never requires a certain ability, or irreversibly loses it? Is a newborn anencephalic baby a person, although it will never think, reason, plan its future, nor have a sense of its own self-identity? Is there any personal life in the patient in the persistent vegetative state? Are they real persons?

So again, the logical status of 'being a person' is far from clear. In one (descriptive) sense 'to be a person' means 'to have a specific property (or a set of properties) which constitute a particular kind of being'. But the perennial contestability of those properties (should they be, e.g., rationality, sentience, self-identity, or an immortal soul?) makes that concept almost entirely irrelevant in the debate on abortion. In another (evaluative) sense, 'to be a person' means 'to be a being equipped with certain value-making properties'. So if a being is a person it means that it has some particular value or a right and because of it we have to behave towards it with respect. But again, this interpretation can easily be challenged: if there is more than one candidate for the value-making property of the person, how is it possible to make a reasonable choice? What is the most relevant value-making property of the person - rationality, sentience, or perhaps self-identity?

There is another serious difficulty with defining a human person. We have to determine what sort of property 'being a person' is. If it is a structural property, then one either is or is not a person. If it is a developmental one, then becoming a person is a process and we are bound to try to define exactly the beginning and the end of that process. Incidentally, the same problem arises if we assume that 'being a person' is a structural property and the emergence of the person in the world is not a process but a sudden event. When precisely does that event take place? If it is not causally related to a particular stage in the development of the human body, it may happen equally at the moment of conception, implantation, quickening, viability, birth, or perhaps some time after birth when a baby begins to be aware of its own identity.

The conclusions to be drawn from this analysis are modest. Though I have no doubts at all that you, they, and also myself are certainly persons I cannot tell precisely when I began and when I will die *as a person*. I know very well that there was a state of the world in which I did not exist and I also know that I am mortal and one day I will die, but the precise moment of my coming into this world and my passing away is not a metaphysical discovery. It is always a particular decision: medical, legal, and, most important of all, moral.

Perhaps these difficulties could be avoided by introducing the category of a potential human being, or a potential person. We may say then that although a zygote is neither an actual human being nor a person, it certainly is a potential human being and a potential person, because in normal circumstances it will turn into a fully developed member of the species *homo sapiens*, and will acquire all the features characteristic of an individual personal life. If we accept this suggestion, then the focus of the discussion shifts from strictly philosophical to strictly moral questions. For it turns out that it is not at all self-evident that the killing of a potential human person is equally wrong as the killing of an actually existing human person.

The concept of a potential human being poses also a considerable philosophical problem. Is there really any substantial difference between an actual and potential person? Do we have any moral obligations towards human beings that are only just conceived? Do we have the same moral obligations towards future generations? If we assume those obligations, this, however, may imply that one of our obligations is the duty to bring them into being. That, at least, is the conclusion reached by R.M. Hare who nevertheless presents a strong moral argument for abortion (Hare, 1993, pp.67-84, pp.147-185). So we do not need to have an adequate definition of the human person to be able to argue for or against abortion.

### Science, metaphysics, and ethics

Let us try to summarise concisely the results of our investigations. The solution of the problem 'When does a human being begin and end' is not a question of a scientific discovery. An embryologist looking through a microscope at a fertilised human cell can see only a transparent particle. He can measure and weigh it, he can determine its specific genetic code, he knows that in normal conditions this cell will undergo all the developmental stages distinctive of our species, and become an individual boy or girl. An embryologist, however, does not see through his microscope any wonderful aura surrounding this particle; he does not see the individual John, Paul, or Margaret. Science thus tries to describe and explain only facts, it neither discovers, nor describes values.

It is possible that the solution of the problem of our personhood is not a matter of science, but of a certain metaphysical discovery. But even a philosopher looking at the same particle through a microscope cannot see a soul in it, because the soul is *a priori* invisible. Nor can he see any person there. If some trickster in a laboratory mixed the contents of the test tubes which contain fertilised eggs of different animal species, it would be difficult to tell a human cell from an animal cell at first sight. All in all, man is also an animal species. Some people believe, however, that this particular human cell is equipped with specific metaphysical properties; that it is God's creation, and therefore it has some absolute moral worth or dignity. It is not just another ordinary organism. It is a unique, magnificent, wonderful creature before whom we should already bend our knee, because it carries the mystery of being. But let us assume that some other philosopher stubbornly claims that a fertilised human egg has not and cannot have any soul nor human dignity, and that the soul appears in foetal life only 14, 40 or 90 days after conception. Let us assume that yet another philosopher claims, authoritatively, that a fertilised egg is not a person at all, but contains only human potential and will become a human person only some time after birth.

Each of them is deeply convinced that he possesses the only knowledge of man's properties. But which of them really possesses the truth? I doubt that this debate can be resolved by way of reason or experiment. And calling upon authorities is not the best way of solving philosophical disputes. Few of the most ardent opponents of abortion realise that neither the New nor the Old Testament contains a single sentence that implies that a foetus is human from the moment of conception. Only at the beginning of the 17th century did a Belgian physician named Thomas Fienus publish a treatise on the formation of the foetus in which he stated that it receives a soul only on the third day after conception (Fienus, 1619). Very shortly after, another physician, Paolo Zacchia, in his work *Questiones Medico-Legales*, stated explicitly that a soul is present in a human body from the moment of conception (Zacchia, 1621). Such were the beginnings of the doctrine that man is a human person from the moment of conception (cf. Reich, 1978, p.13).

Thus, since neither science nor metaphysics provides us with any credible arguments that would ultimately solve the problem of our personhood, a fundamental question emerges: is it possible to settle it at all? If it is a moral problem, then its solution lies in a moral decision, a choice of some particular value-making properties, or of the ideal of man and the good life. Is it, however, possible to make a rational choice from among many competing criteria of personhood or a good life? Is it possible to determine with absolute certainty, which ethical system is better and should be chosen, if we do not want only to choose but to be sure that it was the best possible choice. Alasdair MacIntyre (1975) in his insightful but very pessimistic essay, 'How virtues become vices: values, medicine, and social context' has no doubt that it is impossible. The tragic situation of modern man, says MacIntyre, is, as a matter of fact, a result of profound social changes. The still recently existing, relatively stable, homogeneous morality which determined, among other things, the relationship between the patient and the physician and the ways of solving potential conflicts, has broken down. Medicine has lost its ability to see problems clearly and make appropriate moral decisions in a society where technological development has caused some traditional moral virtues indeed to become vices; in a society where one commonly recognised and respected morality has been replaced by a multitude of emerging competitive moral systems, and where every individual aspires to the right to influence the existing social order. Due to liberalism, secularisation, and the pluralistic character of our culture we are inclined to accept a number of totally different moral points of view, and we acknowledge a multiplicity of possible solutions to our moral problems. MacIntyre writes:

> what makes any protagonist's situation tragic is that he inevitably has to choose between wrong and wrong. It is with this in mind that I have spoken of the physician's moral dilemmas as tragic. The moral resources of his culture, of our own culture, offer no solution for him. What matters most in a period in which human life is tragic is to have the strength to resist false solutions. ... The medical profession ought not therefore to look for solutions to philosophical theorizing; what philosophy has to tell them is precisely why they cannot hope for solutions. For a philosopher to try to go beyond this would be for him to misunderstand either the present situation or the scope and limits of his discipline. A philosopher offering positive moral advice in this situation would be a comic character introduced into a tragedy. (MacIntyre, 1975, pp.110-11)

MacIntyre's concise and clear essay has enormous powers of persuasion. If the arguments he presents are valid, then the choice from among different competing concepts of good, the value of life, or the nature of humanhood would indeed be purely irrational. But is his diagnosis, and the conclusion at which he arrives, really correct? I think that he is entirely right when he says that we live in a society in which there has occurred a certain breakdown of traditional moral structures. But the age in which we live is at the same time the age of the discovery and triumph of reason and the moral autonomy of the individual. Since ready-made solutions to our present moral dilemmas indeed do not exist in the resources of our culture, because such dilemmas could not have been anticipated earlier, it does not mean that we have to abdicate from using our reason. I deeply believe that philosophy has a vital role in this matter even if it is only to explain what the possibilities and limits of rational argument are.

45

Philosophy can make us aware of the fact that the truth in ethics is not the same as the truth in mathematics or in the sciences. It can convince us that everyone is ultimately responsible for his own life. It can reveal to us tacitly accepted value systems, showing us the inevitable conflicts within them; it can explain to us the meaning of certain moral concepts, the functions of the moral language we use, and the possibility of a rational solution to moral problems (Hare, 1993, pp.1-14). Obviously, this does not imply that if we have specific philosophical training, then we can easily resolve all our moral problems. But we can at least see what constitutes them, what the moral price we are ready to pay is and why we may have to decide between evil and evil. Even in the most tragic of lives, in the most tragic of situations, some partial solutions are possible, and the fact that we are not able always rationally to justify them does not yet prove that they are wrong.

This was expressed in an excellent way by Thomas Nagel, who having stated the inevitability of conflict in the choice of a moral perspective asks:

Does this mean, then, that basic practical conflicts have no solution? The unavailability of a single, reductive method or a clear set of priorities for settling them does not remove the necessity for making decisions in such cases. When faced with conflicting and incommensurable claims we still have to do something - even it is only to do nothing. And the fact that action must be unitary seems to imply that unless justification is also unitary, nothing can be either right or wrong and all decisions under conflict are arbitrary.

I believe this is wrong, but the alternative is hard to explain. Briefly, I contend that there can be good judgement without total justification, either explicit or implicit. The fact that one cannot say why a certain decision is the correct one, given a particular balance of conflicting reasons, does not mean that the claim to correctness is meaningless. Provided one has taken the process of practical justification as far as it will go in the course of arriving at the conflict, one may be able to proceed without further justification, but without irrationality either. What makes it possible is *judgment* - essentially the faculty Aristotle described as practical wisdom, which reveals itself over time in individual decisions rather than in the enunciation of general principles. It will not always yield a solution: there are true practical dilemmas that have no solution, and there are also conflicts so complex that judgment cannot operate confidently. But in many cases it can be relied on to take up the slack that remains beyond the limits of explicit rational argument. (Nagel, 1979, pp.134-135)

Thus it is not that there exists one and only one proper solution of the problem of abortion, or that the problem is *a priori* impossible to solve. It may be that there simply exist many better or worse solutions, and only after their scrupulous analysis and assessment, up to the limits of rational argument, should we try to make the best decision, the wisest one in our opinion, which we perhaps cannot always fully justify by rational arguments, but which in the best way reflects our beliefs about the given matter in a specific situation. What, then, is the nature of practical wisdom in solving the abortion problem?

## The wisdom of motherhood

Let us make three essential assumptions. Firstly, let us assume that none of us has a monopoly of moral truth, that hence it is better to discuss it in terms of beliefs rather than knowledge. We have considerably better prospects for discussion and mutual understanding with somebody who *believes* the truth to be so and so than with someone who claims that he *knows* how things are. It will enable us to avoid a certain moral despotism which usually involves moral indoctrination and strong paternalism.

Secondly, let us assume that each of us has a right to have his own moral beliefs. It is thus clear that there may be a variety of approaches concerning the theoretical solution of the problem of abortion - from the most orthodox and conservative to the most radical ones. Personally, I am inclined to accept the principle of potentiality, which claims that it is wrong to kill a potential human being; yet this may not be an argument for someone who accepts a different moral position. Thus in the situation where there are many possible solutions we must choose a particular theory, or a particular moral perspective. Still, this choice does not have to be arbitrary, although it remains beyond the limits of rational argument, as Nagel puts it. How to find out when the choice of a moral perspective is the right one remains a matter of a separate discussion which we shall leave to moral philosophers. For something else is important here: it is important that, since we have assumed that a better or worse decision is possible, then even when we deeply believe that we have made the right decision, we cannot in advance exclude the possibility that we could be wrong. Thus we do not stop thinking, we do not reject the analysis and consideration of other, previously unknown arguments; we remain open to contact with a different moral perspective, with another person.

The third assumption amounts to the distinction between the theoretical and the practical level of the discussion on abortion. On the theoretical level, each of us may have particular opinions on that matter, may accept a particular kind of metaphysics, moral philosophy, or theory of values. But the majority of individuals who adopt various theoretical approaches towards the problem of abortion never face the practical problem - to terminate a pregnancy or to bear a child. It is a practical problem concerning exclusively one woman. So it is the woman and only the woman who is morally responsible for her decision to have or not to have an abortion.

I think, therefore, that each woman has a moral duty to bear a child as far as she considers it her moral obligation. The fact that a physician, philosopher, or priest thinks that a woman should or should not terminate pregnancy does not logically imply that she really has a moral obligation to do so. For there is no direct logical transition from judgements of facts to judgements of values and obligations. If the Pope says (and it is a fact that he says it) that abortion is absolutely wrong, it does not imply that your decision to have an abortion is absolutely wrong. It is always profoundly personal, but it does not have to be an arbitrary decision. Whether a woman does or does not consider giving birth her moral duty may depend on a variety of reasons and some of them are better than others. Here are some examples:

1   The more a woman is morally responsible for the conception of the child, the greater is her moral obligation to give birth. If, for example, the pregnancy is a result of rape, the woman may feel she has no moral responsibility whatsoever for the conception of her child. Hence she can rightly decide that in such a situation giving birth is not her moral obligation. But it may also happen that someone decides that it would be better if the child would be born nevertheless, although conceived through rape. Whatever the woman decides in such a situation, she is the best judge of what is good for her or of what her moral obligation is and her decision should be respected. The same reasoning applies if the pregnancy is, for instance, a result of a failure of contraceptives. On the other hand, however, if somebody deliberately but carelessly decided to conceive, but after a few months, having an opportunity of spending a nice holiday abroad, decides to terminate the pregnancy, probably the majority of us would say it is a poor justification for her decision to abort.

2   The more the delivery may endanger the health and/or life of the mother, the better reasons she has not to consider bearing the child her moral obligation. But, on the other hand, we cannot exclude the possibility that there will be women who wish to have a child at any cost, even at the cost of sacrificing their own lives. We should remember, however, that although each of us has a right to make sacrifices, there are limits of sacrifice. Someone may try to persuade and convince me that I should sacrifice my life for the good of another human being, but nobody can force me to do that, nobody can make it my moral obligation. It is thus admirable that Janusz Korczak joined a group of Jewish children he was caring for on their way to the Treblinka gas chamber, but nobody would

48

have a right to condemn him if he decided not to do so.

3   The greater the probability that giving birth to a child may be harmful to the child, the better reasons a woman has to decide in favour of abortion. I understand, then, and am inclined fully to excuse those women who decided to terminate their pregnancy because of their past exposure to radioactivity (the Chernobyl case), or because they are infected with AIDS. Perhaps in such situations it is better for a child not to be born at all than to live a life full of suffering and indignity. All the so-called genetic indications are very important reasons in making the decision whether to terminate pregnancy.

4   It may also happen that the obligation to bear a child conflicts with other moral obligations. It may happen that the sense of responsibility towards a numerous family living in appalling housing conditions will prevail over the sense of obligation to bear yet another child. It may be that the spectre of overpopulation and the sense of responsibility for the future of the human species will become a sufficiently good reason for a decision in favour of family planning. All the so-called social reasons imply in fact a reference to other values and other moral obligations.

But even if a woman is unable to give any (what we would usually consider to be) good reason, if she simply says she can't have a baby, even then her decision should be respected. She may know better than anyone else why she, with her character and life history, cannot have a baby, even if she cannot explain it in a discursive way. She may have reached a good judgement even though she is unable to explain the way she came to it. We should trust her because she is the captain of the ship - she and only she can be the mother and it is up to her to choose the time and the way of her motherhood. Whatever is her decision she is the person responsible for it and we have no right to deprive her of this responsibility.

## Bibliography

Dennett, D.C. (1981), *Brainstorms: Philosophical Essays on Mind and Psychology*, Harvester Press, Brighton, Sussex.
Fienus, T. (1619), *De Formatrice Foetvs*, Antwerp.
Hare, R.M. (1993), *Essays on Bioethics*, Clarendon Press, Oxford.

MacIntyre, A. (1975), 'How virtues become vices: values, medicine, and social context', in Engelhardt, H.T. Jr and Spicker, S.F. (eds), *Evaluation and Explanation in the Biomedical Sciences*, Reidel Publishing Company, Dordrecht, Holland, pp.97-111.

Nagel, T. (1979), *Mortal Questions*, Cambridge University Press, Cambridge.

Reich, W. (ed.) (1978), *Encylopedia of Bioethics* Vol. 1, Collier Macmillan Publishers, London.

Zacchia, P. (1621), *Questiones Medico-Legales*, Lyons.

# 4 The right to die, advance directives and euthanasia

*Bridgit Dimond*

Despite the pressure of moral philosophers who maintain that there is no moral distinction between killing and letting die, the law has remained firm in drawing a clear distinction between allowing a death to take place and taking steps to bring life to an end. This paper looks at the basic principles of the law relating to euthanasia and considers the topics set out below:

1 Definitions of voluntary euthanasia, and passive and active euthanasia.

2 Basic principles of the law concerning murder, manslaughter and suicide.

3 Principles relating to consent, as found in the law relating to mentally competent adults, the law relating to mentally incompetent adults and adults in a persistent vegetative state, the Law Commission proposals, the law relating to severely disabled children, to consent by the mentally competent child, and to the elderly.

4 Advance refusals of treatment.

5 Switching off and switching on life support machines.

6 Not For Resuscitation (NFR) instructions.

7 Extraordinary treatment and ordinary treatment.

8 Quality of life issues.

Some concluding remarks will follow these considerations.

## Definitions

When the topic of euthanasia arises, discussion normally focuses on voluntary active euthanasia, where a person of mental competence has requested that he or she is allowed to die and requests the assistance of another person. This is known as voluntary euthanasia. It could be passive in the sense that care is withheld or active in the sense that death is actively brought about e.g. by medication, suffocation or removing vital lifesaving treatment such as a life support machine. In this paper we are concerned with all forms of euthanasia since the recent cases of Tony Bland and some cases involving children have raised issues relating to the ending of life of those who are not dying but do not have the capacity or the means to give consent.

## Basic principles: murder, manslaughter and suicide

At present the law clearly states that it is illegal to take actions to bring about the death of another person and, unless one of the clear exceptions to this principle exists, to bring about the death of another person is murder. Nor is it lawful to assist another person in committing suicide.

The definition of murder is:

> ... when a man of sound memory, and of the age of discretion, unlawfully killeth within any country of the realm any reasonable creature *in rerum natura* under the king's peace, with malice aforethought, either expressed by the party or implied by law, so as the party wounded, or hurt etc. die of the wound or hurt, etc. within a year and a day after the same. (Coke, 3 Inst 47, cited in Dine and Gobert, 1993, p.388)

It should be noted that this is likely to be changed when the time limit of one year and a day is removed as recommended by the Law Commission.

There is a mandatory life sentence of anyone over 18 years who is convicted of murder.

Voluntary manslaughter exists when the ingredients for murder are present but there are exceptional circumstances such as:

1 Provocation

2 Death in pursuance of a suicide pact

3 Diminished responsibility

Involuntary manslaughter exists when the mental intention (i.e. *mens rea*) to

52

cause death is missing. Thus in cases of gross negligence, death may result but there is no intention to kill. Killing recklessly may or may not be sufficient to be murder. If the accused has acted with reckless regard to the possibility that death might occur from his actions, judged on an objective basis, then a charge of murder may arise, otherwise a manslaughter charge would be brought. An intention to escape from lawful arrest which results in a death would also be grounds for a manslaughter charge.

The judge has the discretion following a verdict of guilty of manslaughter to sentence the convicted person to anything from absolute discharge to imprisonment for a considerable length of time, as well as any order under Part 3 of the Mental Health Act 1983.

Even though suicide was no longer a crime after the passing of the Suicide Act 1961, to assist or aid another person in a suicide attempt remained illegal. Section 2(1) of the Suicide Act 1961 is as follows:

A person who aids, abets, counsels or procures the suicide of another or an attempt by another to commit suicide, shall be liable on conviction on indictment to imprisonment (up to 14 years).

This means that where any health professional or indeed anyone else is asked by a person to assist in bringing about his or her death, and obliges, this is a criminal act. This is so even where the person making the request is terminally ill. It also applies to those who give advice. Thus there were convictions under the Suicide Act of those who printed a book advising people on how to end their lives.

Some philosophers have criticised the distinction which is drawn in the law between killing a person and allowing a person to die (Cf. Rachels, 1971; Harris, 1985), arguing that the outcome is the same. However the distinction is at the heart of the decision of the House of Lords permitting the artificial feeding of Tony Bland to cease (see below). Lord Browne-Wilkinson addressed the dilemma:

How can it be lawful to allow a patient to die slowly, though painlessly, over a period of weeks from lack of food but unlawful to produce his immediate death by a lethal injection, thereby saving his family from yet another ordeal to add to the tragedy that has already struck them? I find it difficult to find a moral answer to that question. But it is undoubtedly the law and nothing I have said casts doubt on the proposition that the doing of a positive act with the intention of ending life is and remains murder. (Airedale NHS Trust v. Bland [1993], p.884)

## Principles relating to consent

### Mentally competent adults

Against the clear principles of the criminal law must be set the principles of trespass to the person. It is an unlawful act, a civil wrong, for one individual to touch another person without his or her consent. The definition of trespass to the person is as follows:

> An act of the defendant which directly and either intentionally or negligently causes either some physical contact with the person of the plaintiff without the plaintiff's consent (this is known as a battery) or causes the plaintiff immediately to apprehend a contact with his person (this is known as an assault). (Brazier, 1988)

The plaintiff is the person suing for compensation in the civil courts.

If a mentally competent adult refused to give consent to treatment, even though it is lifesaving, then that treatment would constitute a trespass to the person. The Court of Appeal has recently confirmed this basic concept in the case of *Re T* (1992). In another recent case (*Re C* [1994]) involving a patient at Broadmoor Hospital it was held that he had the right to refuse an operation to amputate his leg, even though doctors believed the operation to be a lifesaving necessity. It was established that the patient had the capacity to make a valid decision and an injunction was ordered to prevent any person carrying out the amputation without the consent of the patient.

If therefore a mentally competent person who is terminally ill refuses to have lifesaving treatment, that refusal must be respected even if the outcome is death.

We thus have two parallel situations. A person can commit suicide without committing a criminal offence. However no-one is able to assist him in that suicide. That would constitute a criminal offence. A mentally competent adult who is dying can refuse lifesaving treatment, and it would be a civil wrong for any one to give treatment to that person against his will.

### Mentally incompetent adults including those in persistent vegetative states

If an adult is not capable of giving consent then the health professional must act in the best interests of that person. This was the ruling by the House of Lords in the case of F. v. West Berkshire Health Authority (1989), where it was held that:

> ... a doctor can lawfully operate on or give other treatment to adult patients who are incapable of consenting to his doing so, provided that the

54

operation or treatment is in the best interests of such patients. [That is] ...
if it is carried out either to save their lives or to ensure improvement or
prevent deterioration in their physical or mental health. (F. v. West
Berkshire HA [1989], p.546)

Acting in the best interests of an individual may involve withholding treatment
if the prognosis is intolerable.

Where the patient is in a persistent vegetative state, then the House of Lords
has held that artificial feeding could cease, since that constituted treatment
(Cf. Airedale NHS Trust v. Bland, [1993]). This was the ruling in the case
of Tony Bland who had never recovered consciousness since the Hillsborough
stadium disaster. Following that decision practice directions were issued by
the court setting out the procedure to be followed in the case of relatives
and/or health professionals seeking for treatment to cease where the patient
was in a persistent vegetative state (Practice note, [1994]).

*Law Commission proposals*

Consultation has been taking place since 1991 over proposals by the Law
Commission to fill the vacuum which currently exists in law to make
decisions on behalf of the mentally incompetent adult. An initial consultation
document giving an overview (Law Commission, 1991) was followed by more
detailed proposals for consultation (Law Commission, 1993A, 1993B, 1993C)
and final proposals were contained in a report which contained draft
legislation (Law Commission, 1995). The essence of its proposals is that
decisions which need to be made about the wellbeing, property, treatment etc.
for a mentally incapacitated adult should be made according to a hierarchy of
decision makers. Day to day decisions may be made by a carer, other
decisions could be made by a person with statutory authority, more serious
decisions would be made by a judicial forum. If their proposals are
implemented, decisions relating to those in persistent vegetative states or
comparable conditions would come before the recommended judicial forum.

*Severely disabled children*

The Law Commission reports cited above were concerned only with adults
and life and death decisions relating to children will continue to rest with the
High Court in accordance with the principles established in the Children Act
1989, other statutory provisions and the common law.

It is unlawful for any person to take positive action to bring the life of a
severely disabled child to an end. This was stated by the judge in the trial of
Dr Arthur for attempting to cause the death of a Down's syndrome child with

55

other disabilities (R. v. Arthur, [1981]). He prescribed dihydrocodeine. He was acquitted of causing the death of the child, in what some have seen as a perverse jury verdict. The judge stated that:

> There is no special law in this country that places doctors in a separate category and gives them extra protection over the rest of us. Neither, in law, is there any special power, facility or licence to kill children who are handicapped or seriously disadvantaged in an irreversible way. (R. v. Arthur, [1981], quoted in Kennedy and Grubb, 1989, p.1248)

*Consent by the mentally competent child*

A child of 16 or 17 has a statutory right to give consent under the Family Law Reform Act 1969. A child of any age has a right at common law to give consent to treatment as a result of the principles laid down by the House of Lords in the Gillick case (Gillick v. West Norfolk and Wisbech AHA, [1985]). This held that a mentally competent child who had the maturity to understand the implications of a decision could give a valid consent without the involvement of parents. However it does not appear that a child of 16 or 17, or one who is Gillick competent, has the ability in law to refuse treatment which is in her or his best interests. This was the situation in the case of *Re W* (1992) where a girl of 16 years suffered from anorexia nervosa and refused to accept treatment. The Court of Appeal decided that it was in her best interests to receive this treatment and made the appropriate order.

It is highly unlikely therefore that a child who has the mental competence would be permitted to take a decision which is contrary to her or his best interests if a life and death decision has to be made. Thus in a recent case a boy of $15^3/_4$ (*Re E*, [1993]) who was a Jehovah's Witness refused to have blood and this refusal was supported by his parents but the court held that he should be given it, in spite of the fact that he was so close to his sixteenth birthday.

There are several Court of Appeal decisions where it has made declarations supporting the principle that, where it is in the interests of the child, the doctor need not give active treatment to a child who was dying, or who, even if not dying, had an intolerable existence.

A summary of the main principles which emerge from these cases, together with the facts of each case is given below:

*A doctor does not have to prolong the life of a dying child* An example of the court permitting a child to be allowed to die is the case of *Re C* (1989). In this case a baby was born suffering from congenital hydrocephalus and had been made a ward of court for reasons unconnected with her medical condition. The local authority sought the court's determination as to the appropriate manner in which she should be treated, should she contract a serious infection, or her existing feeding regimes become unviable. A specialist paediatrician assessed C's condition as severely and irreversibly brain-damaged, the prognosis of which was hopeless. He recommended that the objective of any treatment should therefore be to ease suffering rather than prolong life. While not specifying the adoption or discontinuance of any particular procedures, he further advised consultation with C's carers as to the appropriate method of achieving that objective. The judge accepted this report and approved the recommendations as being in her best interests. He initially made a very restrictive order to treat the child to die. But these words 'to die' were changed to 'to allow her life to come to an end peacefully and with dignity'.

The official solicitor, who had been appointed guardian ad litem of the child, appealed to the Court of Appeal on the ground that the judge had no jurisdiction and was plainly wrong in the exercise of his discretion to make an order that the hospital be at liberty to treat the minor to die. The Court of Appeal varied the judge's order and substituted the words:

> That the hospital authority do continue to treat the minor within the parameters of the opinion expressed by [the specialist paediatrician] in his report of 13.iv.1989 which report is not to be disclosed to any person other than the hospital authority. (Re C [1989], p.788)

*Even where the child is not on the point of death active treatment does not have to be given* In *Re J* (1990) the baby was a ward of court and in contrast with the case of *Re C* (1989) the baby was not at the point of death. However the prognosis was not good and although he was expected to survive a few years he was likely to be blind, deaf, unable to speak and have serious spastic quadriplegia. The judge made an order that he should be treated with antibiotics if he developed a chest infection but if he were to stop breathing he should not receive artificial ventilation. The official solicitor on behalf of the child appealed against the order on the grounds that unless the situation was one of terminal illness or it was certain that the child's life would be intolerable, the court was not justified in approving the withholding of lifesaving treatment. The court held that the court can never sanction positive steps to terminate the life of a person. However the court could direct that treatment without which death would ensue need not be given to prolong life, even though he was neither on the point of death nor dying. The Court had to undertake a balancing exercise in assessing the course to be adopted in the best interests of the child, looked at from his point of view and giving the fullest possible weight to his desire, if he were in a position to make a sound judgement to survive, and taking into account the pain and suffering and quality of life which he would experience if life was prolonged and the pain and suffering involved in the proposed treatment.

*The court will not order a doctor to take action contrary to what the doctor considers to be in the child's best interests* This was stated by the Court of Appeal in the case of *Re J* (1992). It had to decide if a child who was born in January 1991 and had suffered an accidental fall when he was a month old, with the result that he was profoundly handicapped both mentally and physically, should be placed on artificial ventilation. The mother supported the requirement that the hospital and doctors should be forced to put the baby on a life support machine.

Lord Donaldson, Master of the Rolls, stated that he could not at present conceive of any circumstances in which to require a medical practitioner or health authority acting by a medical practitioner to adopt a course of treatment which in the bona fide clinical judgement of the practitioner was contra-indicated as not being in the patient's best interests, would be other than an abuse of power as directly or indirectly requiring the practitioner to act contrary to the fundamental duty he owed to his patient (*Re J* [1992], p.622).

Lord Donaldson said that the order of the judge, directing specific treatment to take place, was wholly inconsistent with the law (*Re J* [1992], p.623). The Court of Appeal held that where a paediatrician caring for a severely handicapped baby considered that mechanical ventilation procedures would not be appropriate the court would not grant an injunction requiring such treatment to take place.

There are therefore several Court of Appeal decisions which have enabled the doctors to permit a severely disabled child to die. None however have authorised positive action to be taken to speed up the death.

One difficulty which arises is that the action is likely to come before the courts only if there is a dispute between parents and professionals, or the child is already a ward of court or under the care of the local authority, or if the professionals themselves seek a declaration from the courts to ensure that their actions or omissions are legally sanctioned. There are probably many cases in neonatal units where similar decisions are taken without court authority and it may be that different units use different criteria for decisions on withholding treatment. This is not a satisfactory state of affairs and greater certainty on the legal situation is required as has occurred in the case of patients in a persistent vegetative state following the Tony Bland decision and the issue of Practice Directions (see above).

The same principles which apply to the mentally competent adult apply to the mentally competent elderly person. In contrast to the verdict in the case of Dr Arthur, Dr Cox was convicted of a criminal offence and sentenced to a year's imprisonment suspended for a year (R. v. Cox, [1993]). He had prescribed potassium chloride to a dying patient who was racked by pain. He also faced disciplinary proceedings brought by his employers, Wessex Regional Health Authority, and also professional conduct proceedings brought by the General Medical Council, but he retained both his post and his registration.

Exactly the same principles apply to the rights of the elderly as they do to younger adults. However in practice there is a tendency for professionals to place them in a different category, particularly if dying. Thus the relatives may be told the prognosis in advance of the patient, a reversal of the practice which should be followed. Ambulance officers may receive instructions not to take a person over a particular age to a cardiac unit, but instead take him or her to a geriatric ward. Similarly Not For Resuscitation orders may be given in respect of those above an arbitrary age limit. Such rules and practices made irrespective of the particular circumstances of the individual patient are not lawful and acceptable and may be contrary to the best interests of the patient.

*The mentally incompetent elderly person* Relatives may sometimes be asked for their opinion about whether or not treatment should be given to an elderly person who is no longer capable of giving consent. In law the relative does not have a legal right to give or withhold consent. (After all, who knows what the personal interests of the relative may be? He or she may be looking to inherit.) In the absence of any capacity of the patient to make a decision or any advance directions (see below), the doctor must act in the best interests of the patient. This is the implication of the decision of the House of Lords in *Re F* (F. v. West Berkshire HA, [1989]).

The best interests of the patient is determined by applying the Bolam Test (cf. Bolam v. Friern Hospital Management Committee, [1957]), which asks what would any reasonable professional following the accepted approved standard of care determine would be in the interests of the patient?

### Advance refusals of treatment

At present, there are no statutory provisions applying to advance refusals of treatment. The House of Lords (in the Bland case) recognised that an advance refusal of treatment may be valid and should be taken into account in determining the treatment to be given to an incompetent person. In its political capacity the Select Committee of the House of Lords (House of Lords Select Committee on Medical Ethics, 1994) in its report on medical ethics supported the development of advance directives but concluded that legislation is unnecessary and suggested instead that the colleges and faculties of all the health-care professions should jointly develop a code of practice to guide their members. As a consequence the British Medical Association has put forward a Code of Practice (see below) (British Medical Association, 1995).

## The Law Commission's proposals

The Law Commission in its final report on *Mental Incapacity* (Law Commission, 1995) suggested that there should be legislation covering the situation. What is now proposed by the Law Commission is a statutory basis for an advance refusal of treatment. This covers a refusal by a person, who has attained the age of 18 and has the necessary capacity, to any medical, surgical or dental treatment or other procedure, being a refusal intended to have effect at any subsequent time when he may be without capacity to give or refuse his consent.

Unless an advance refusal of treatment specifically covers the following, it will be assumed that the refusal does not apply if the refusal: (a) endangers that person's life; or (b) endangers the life of the foetus (should the person be pregnant).

A person is protected in law if he withholds treatment on the basis that he has reasonable grounds for believing that that treatment is covered by an advance refusal or if he gives treatment not knowing or having reasonable grounds for believing that an advance refusal of treatment covers that treatment or procedure.

*Format of an advance refusal of treatment*  The Law Commission (Law Commission, 1995, para. 5.30, p.78) proposes that a refusal may take the form of an instrument in writing and, in the absence of any indication to the contrary, it shall be presumed that an advance refusal of treatment was validly made if it is signed by the person by whom it is made and by at least one other person as a witness to his signature. However this is 'without prejudice to any other method of expressing an advance refusal of treatment' (Law Commission, 1995, para. 5.30, p.78), so other forms may also be accepted as valid. This could include an expression by word of mouth if witnesses are present.

*Revocation*  The Law Commission propose that an advance refusal of treatment may at any time be withdrawn or altered by the person who made it if he then has the capacity to do so (Law Commission, 1995, para. 5.32, p.79). No formalities are laid down.

*Exclusions for the advance refusal*  The Law Commission propose that the advance refusal of treatment shall not preclude the following treatment being given:

1  The provision of basic care. This is defined as 'care to maintain bodily cleanliness and to alleviate severe pain and the provision of direct oral nutrition and hydration' (Law Commission, 1995, para. 5.34, p.79).

2  Taking any action necessary to prevent death or a serious deterioration in his condition pending a decision of the court on the validity or applicability of an advance refusal of treatment or on the question whether it has been withdrawn or altered (Law Commission, 1995, para. 5.36, p.80).

The Law Commission suggests that the court should have the power to make a declaration on whether an advance refusal of treatment has been validly made, withdrawn or altered, including the capacity of the individual to make, withdraw or alter it (Law Commission, 1995, para. 5.36, p.80).

*British Medical Association proposals*

The British Medical Association has recently published a Code of Practice (British Medical Association, 1995) for its members on advance statements about medical treatment. It gives guidance on the law in relation to consent to medical treatment and advance statements and advice on the drafting and contents of an advance statement. It emphasises that there must be no pressure on patients. It also gives guidance about determining the patient's capacity to make decisions. The responsibility for storing an advance directive is upon the individual but it is suggested that a copy should be given to the general practitioner. Finally a check list is provided for making an advance directive and this is shown in figure 1.

*Present situation*

Until the proposals of the Law Commission are enacted, the common law prevails. It is advisable therefore for every NHS Trust to ensure that its staff have guidance on advising patients about the law relating to living wills. The following points should be emphasised:

In drawing up an advance statement you must ensure, as a minimum, that the following information is included:

* Full name
* Address
* Name and address of general practitioner
* Whether advice was sought from health professionals
* Signature
* Date drafted and reviewed
* Witness signature
* A clear statement of your wishes, either general or specific
* The name, address and telephone number of your nominated person, if you have one.

*Source:* British Medical Association (1995) p.39

**Figure 1    British Medical Association check list for writing an advance statement**

1   Every adult mentally competent patient has the right to give and withhold consent to treatment.

2   Such decisions can be made in advance but it is advisable for the patient to have assistance in preparing any such advance directions.

3   Staff should be warned that to ignore the clearly expressed advance statements by patients could constitute a trespass to the person or even a criminal offence.

4   The present law on the illegality of euthanasia is not changed. It is unlawful to kill an individual or to assist in their suicide. Thus to administer medication with the intention of shortening life is illegal.

It is not however unlawful to withhold lifesaving medication on the basis of the refusal of the patient whether that refusal is expressed at the time or in advance. The distinction in law between letting die, which may in certain circumstances be lawful, and killing is maintained.

Previous statutes such as the Abortion Act 1967 and the Human Fertilisation and Embryology Act 1990 have conscientious objection clauses which enable a person to opt out of carrying out treatment to which they conscientiously object except in an emergency situation. Could a nurse or a doctor refuse to acknowledge an advance refusal of treatment on the grounds that they have a conscientious objection, possibly based on their Code of Professional Practice, to allowing a person to act contrary to their best interests? There is no such clause included in the draft legislation provided by the Law Commission (Law Commission, 1995). Nor could such a clause be contemplated. The fact that an adult mentally competent person refuses treatment must prevail against the views of the professional caring for him. Thus for a nurse or doctor to argue that a Jehovah's Witness must be given blood in a lifesaving situation is contrary to the present law of consent and the same principle must apply to advance directions. There is therefore no room for an exception for professionals on the ground of conscientious objection. The suggestion by the Law Commission (1995, para. 5.34, p.79) that an advance refusal cannot cover basic care should meet the professional requirements of many health professionals.

## Switching off and switching on life support machines

Legally it could be argued that exactly the same principles apply to switching off life support machines as apply to the switching on; i.e. if there is a duty to provide care in that the patient has not refused consent, and the circumstances are such that the prognosis is reasonably good and the quality of life of a reasonable standard, then the machine must be switched on or, if already on, cannot be switched off at that point.

Difficulties however arise, especially in emergency admissions, where the life support machine has been switched on by a person attending the crisis, when it is not appropriate. In these circumstances, switching off the machine becomes a matter of significant action. In the case of Karen Quinlan (*Re Quinlan*, [1976]; cf. Kennedy and Grubb, 1989, pp.963-4 and pp.1107-10) in the United States the parents of an insensate patient requested that the machine be switched off. The case and the appeals lasted a considerable time and when eventually discontinuance was ordered, she survived for several years off the machine.

## Not for resuscitation instructions

As long as the prognosis of the patient is reasonable and the adult competent patient has not made it clear that he refuses treatment whether at the time or by means of an advance refusal of treatment, the professional has a duty to take all reasonable care of the patient, and in certain cases this may involve providing resuscitation. If the prognosis is good, and there is no valid refusal of treatment by the patient, failure to resuscitate could in certain circumstances be a criminal act.

Where however the doctor is of the view that in the light of the prognosis or the quality of life that the patient would have, or where the patient has made a clear refusal of resuscitative treatment, a Not For Resuscitation (NFR) or Do Not Resuscitate (DNR) instruction is valid. Difficulties can arise, where for example such instructions are not given in writing by doctors to nursing staff or where nurses have not had an input into the decision making and are not aware of or disagree with, the basis of the NFR/DNR instruction. A report has been issued by the Royal College of Nursing (RCN Ethics and Nursing Committee, 1992) which sets out the moral and legal issues and strongly endorses the involvement of the health care professional team as well as the patient, relatives and friends. Discussions should continue over sufficient time to allow everyone involved to think through the issues. Unfortunately, given the short length of stay that patients have on the wards, and the high proportion of emergency admissions, in many cases time will not enable protracted discussions to take place and decisions have to be made urgently in the heat of the crisis (cf. Dimond, 1992).

## Extraordinary treatment and ordinary treatment

Since the law permits certain treatments to be discontinued where the duty to keep the patient alive no longer exists, it is important to determine which treatments and care can be ended. In the Tony Bland case, the House of Lords held that medical treatment, including artificial feeding and the administration of antibiotic drugs could lawfully be withheld from an insensate patient with no hope of recovery. In discussing the issue as to whether artificial feeding was medical treatment Lord Goff of Cheiveley said:

> Objection can be made to the latter course of action [i.e. discontinuing artificial feeding] on the ground that Anthony will thereby be starved to death, and this would constitute a breach of the duty to feed him which must form an essential part of the duty which every person owes to another in his care. But here again it is necessary to analyse precisely

what this means in the case of Anthony. Anthony is not merely incapable of feeding himself. He is incapable of swallowing, and therefore of eating or drinking in the normal sense of those words. There is overwhelming evidence that, in the medical profession, artificial feeding is regarded as a form of medical treatment; and, even if it is not strictly medical treatment, it must form part of the medical care of the patient. Indeed, the function of artificial feeding in the case of Anthony, by means of a nasogastric tube, is to provide a form of life support analogous to that provided by a ventilator which artificially breathes air in and out of the lungs of a patient incapable of breathing normally, thereby enabling oxygen to reach the bloodstream. (Airedale NHS Trust v. Bland [1993], pp.870-1)

Medical treatment is therefore what is provided as part of the medical care of the patient. This must however be distinguished from nursing care. Thus in its final report on Mental Incapacity (Law Commission, 1995), the Law Commission opposed the idea that a person could by means of an advance refusal of treatment refuse basic nursing care, i.e. 'care to maintain bodily cleanliness and to alleviate severe pain and the provision of direct oral nutrition and hydration' (Law Commission, 1995, para. 5.34, p.79).

Terms such as 'extraordinary treatment' which could be discontinued and 'ordinary care or treatment' which cannot be discontinued are not necessarily helpful. There may be some patients, suffering from a chronic condition who are on permanent artificial feeding or artificial ventilation and what could be withheld from such patients in the event of their becoming insensate may therefore be different from those who are not regularly on such support.

It is notable that in the case of Re J (1992), discussed above, the Court of Appeal was reluctant to tell the doctor what he should or should not withhold. However it is likely that if Tony Bland could have taken food and drink by mouth, the House of Lords would not have authorised this to be withheld.

The situation thus arises that if a person does not require artificial forms of support for feeding and breathing, then that individual may survive for many years with an extremely low quality of life (since it is illegal to take positive action to bring about the person's death). This point was made by the Creedon parents who blamed the doctors for being prepared to withhold antibiotics from their son, but as long as he could feed himself, and did not suffer an infection, there was no way in which his life could be ended (The Times, 1 August 1995). Their application for the child to be made a ward of court was accepted and a hearing is now awaited on whether the court will permit positive action for the child's life to be ended.

## Quality of life issues

These arose in some of the child cases, especially *Re J* (1990) where the child was not dying but it was agreed that extraordinary measures such as artificial ventilation need not be commenced if doctors considered that it was not in his best interests.

It has risen more starkly in the case of Creedon where the parents maintain that the child should not be kept alive. However since the child is not being artificially fed and is not on artificial ventilation it was not possible to cease to provide extraordinary measures in order to allow the child to die. As the parents have said: antibiotics would not be given if the child had an infection, but no action can be taken to shorten his life (cf. *The Times*, 1 August 1995).

## Causation and causing death

This issue has arisen in cases where a person is charged with a criminal offence which results in the victim being placed on a life support machine. When this has been turned off and the patient dies and a murder charge then brought, the criminal has used the defence that he did not cause death, but the switching off of the life support machine was the cause. In the cases where this has been argued the defence has failed (R. v. Malcherek, [1981]; R. v. Steel, [1981]), on the grounds that at the time of conventional death, after the life support machinery was disconnected, the original wound or injury was a continuing, operating and indeed substantial cause of the death of the victim.

The question also arose for discussion in the Tony Bland case, where the House of Lords considered if the doctors would be guilty of bringing about the death of the patient were they to discontinue the artificial feeding. Lord Mustill accepted that there may be causative conduct by the doctors:

> It does not perhaps follow that the conduct of the doctors is not also causative, but this is of no interest since if the conduct is lawful the doctors have nothing to worry about. (Airedale NHS Trust v. Bland [1993], p.893)

## Conclusions

The law is skating across some tortuous philosophical issues and there is pressure for the law to recognise that there is no legal distinction between letting die and killing. The House of Lords Select Committee (House of Lords Select Committee on Medical Ethics, 1994) has resisted the pressure to bring in voluntary euthanasia.

Other matters are uncertain however. For example, that of when it is necessary to obtain the declaration of the court before letting a child or mentally incapacitated adult die. In the case of persistent vegetative state the court has been clear and a procedure for involving the court has been drawn up. There are however many other conditions in which the parents and professionals or relatives and professionals may decide that the patient can be allowed to die, which never become the subject of court proceedings unless a third person brings the case to the attention of the police or prosecution authority or the health professionals themselves decide to seek the declaration of the court in order to clarify the situation. The recommendations of the Law Commission on the decision making on behalf of the mentally incapacitated adult (Law Commission, 1995), may resolve the situation for the adult, but uncertainties relating to the court involvement in decisions relating to the care of the child still exist.

## Bibliography

*Airedale NHS Trust v. Bland* House of Lords [1993] 1 All ER 821.

*Bolam v. Friern Hospital Management Committee* [1957] 2 All ER 118.

Brazier, M. (1988), *Street on Tort*, Butterworths, London.

British Medical Association (1995), *Advance Statements About Medical Treatment: Code of Practice*, British Medical Association.

*C (a minor)(wardship; medical treatment), Re* [1989] 2 All ER 782.

*C (adult: refusal of medical treatment), Re* Family Division [1994] 1 All ER 819.

Coke, E. *Institutes of the Laws of England* cited in Dine, J. and Gobert, J. (1993), *Cases and Materials on Criminal Law*, Blackstone Press Limited, London.

Dimond, B. (1992), 'Not for resuscitative treatment', *British Journal of Nursing* Vol. 1, No. 2, pp.93-4.

*E (a minor)(wardship: medical treatment), Re* Family Division [1993] 1 FLR 386.

*F. v. West Berkshire HA* [1989] 2 All ER 545.

*Gillick v. West Norfolk and Wisbech AHA* [1985] 3 All ER 402.

Harris, J. (1985), *The Value of Life*, Routledge and Kegan Paul, London.

House of Lords Select Committee on Medical Ethics (1994), *House of Lords Session 1993-94. Report of the Select Committee on Medical Ethics*, Volume 1, HMSO, London.

*J (a minor)(wardship; medical treatment), Re* [1990] 3 All ER 930.

*J (a minor)(wardship: medical treatment), Re* [1992] 4 All ER 614.

Kennedy, I. and Grubb, A. (1989), *Medical Law: Text and Materials* Butterworths, London.

Law Commission (1991), *Decision Making and the Mentally Incapacitated Adult: An Overview. Consultation Paper No. 119*, HMSO, London.

Law Commission (1993A), *Mentally Incapacitated Adults and Decision Making: A New Jurisdiction. Consultation Paper No. 128*, HMSO, London.

Law Commission (1993B), *Mentally Incapacitated Adults and Decision Making: Medical Treatment and Research. Consultation Paper No. 129*, HMSO, London.

Law Commission (1993C), *Mentally Incapacitated and Other Vulnerable Adults: Public Law Protection. Consultation Paper No. 130*, HMSO, London.

Law Commission (1995), *Mental Incapacity. Item 9 of 4th Programme of Law Reform. No. 231*, HMSO, London.

Practice note [1994] 2 All ER 413.

*Quinlan, Re* 355 A 2d 647 [1976].

*R. v. Arthur* [1981] 12 BMLR 1 (Leicester CC); cited in Kennedy and Grubb (1989) pp.1247-49.

*R. v. Cox* [1993] 2 All ER 19.

*R. v. Malcherek* [1981] 2 All ER 422.

*R. v. Steel* [1981] 1 WLR 690, CA.

Rachels, J. (ed.) (1971), *Moral Problems*, Harper and Row, New York.

RCN Ethics and Nursing Committee (1992), *Resuscitation: Right or Wrong? The Moral and Legal Issues Faced By Health Care Professionals*, Royal College of Nursing, London.

*T (adult: refusal of treatment), Re* [1992] 3 WLR 782.

*W (a minor)(medical treatment), Re* [1992] 4 All ER 206.

# Part Two

# HEALTH, DISEASE AND ABNORMALITY

# 5 Concepts of health, illness and disease

*David Greaves*

Health, illness and disease are the three most familiar concepts which are commonly used in the field of medicine and health care. Hence our understanding of the way they are to be defined would seem of fundamental importance, as suggested by a typical introductory statement from a collection of articles on 'Concepts of Health and Disease':

> Disease and health function as directions for health care. Health is that which is to be preserved, restored, and augmented. Views of what count as health will, as a consequence, direct programs aimed at preserving health.
>
> So too, will concepts of disease direct programs aimed at the prevention, care or amelioration of disease states. (Caplan, Engelhardt Jr. and McCartney, 1981, p.xxiii)

Others though dispute the relevance and so the importance of theoretical attempts at defining these concepts, arguing that they reflect practice rather than influencing it, and as such are at best a loose and ever-changing set of ideas. Miller Brown expresses this view: 'It is the practical and changing character of medicine and its language that frustrates the efforts of philosophers to formulate such definitions' (Miller Brown, 1985, p.311).

However it is not necessary to see these concepts as being either on the one hand solely fixed theoretical constructs, or on the other merely pale and rather empty reflections of practice. A different and richer view would suggest that a continuous interaction and development takes place, and that these pervasive concepts have a central role in how it proceeds, so that they both play a part in the definition of the language of medicine and health care, but are also constantly reformulated as part of the ongoing conceptualisation of both theory and practice. Engelhardt describes this dual role as follows:

> The concepts [of health and disease] are ambiguous, operating as

explanatory and evaluatory notions. They describe states of affairs, factual conditions, while at the same time judging them to be good or bad. Health and disease are normative as well as descriptive. (Engelhardt Jr., 1975, p.125)

Nordenfelt also suggests that the role played by concepts of health, illness and disease is not always rational or coherent in practice (Nordenfelt, 1993A). This more complex notion then allows that their characterisation is important, though not in an attempt to discover exact and unitary definitions, but rather to explore different approaches in the recognition that most people, lay and professional, operate with only fragmentary and provisional ideas about them. Nordenfelt further justifies the detailed analysis of these concepts, not only as an intellectual exercise, but because in a subtle and complex way they:

(a) Play important roles in scientific and social as well as medical contexts.
(b) Have important ethical, social and economic consequences e.g. what counts as a disease label, and how this is applied clinically. (Nordenfelt, 1993A)

Now if the ultimate goal of medicine is concerned with the improvement of health, then it might seem logical to focus on the concept of health first, before considering how illness and disease relate to it. But this approach is fraught with difficulties which illustrate just how problematic it is to get a firm grasp on the concept of health. Consider first the following quotation from Nietzsche:

For there is no health as such, and all attempts to define anything in that way have been miserable failures. Even the determination of what health means for your *body* depends on your goal, your horizon, your energies, your drives, your errors, and above all on the ideals and phantasms of your soul. Thus there are innumerable healths of the body: and ... the more we put aside the dogma of the 'equality of men', the more must the concept of a normal health, along with a normal diet and the normal course of an illness be abandoned by our physicians. Only then would the time have come to reflect on the health and sickness of the *soul*, and to find the peculiar virtue of each man in the health of his soul: in one person's case this health could, of course, look like the opposite of health in another person. (Nietzsche, quoted in Downie, 1994, p.184)

What Nietzsche is drawing attention to is the question of how any one absolute definition of health could be possible, when each individual brings his or her own values to the concept in relation to their individual experience of their own health. However recognising that health is an evaluative concept which individuals may assess differently does not preclude there being social or cultural definitions of health which are held in common and gain wide acceptance.

Historically two such contrasting definitions can be identified, which derive from the Greek myths of Hygeia and Asclepius, and contain two general notions of how the goals of medicine and the concept of health may be understood. Dubos views them as symbolising:

... the never-ending oscillation between two different points of view in medicine. For the worshippers of Hygeia, health is the natural order of things, a positive attribute to which men are entitled if they govern their lives wisely. According to them, the most important function of medicine is to discover and teach the natural laws which will ensure to man a healthy mind in a healthy body. More sceptical or wiser in the ways of the world, the followers of Asclepius believe that the chief role of the physician is to treat disease, to restore health by correcting any imperfection caused by the accident of birth or of life. (Dubos, 1960, p.131)

In modern parlance Asclepius and Hygeia relate to medical or biostatistical, and holistic theories of health respectively, the main features of which Nordenfelt has summarised as follows:

First in the biostatistical theory:
1. The concept of disease is defined in biological and statistical terms as a bodily state causing subnormal functioning in the individual.
2. Health is defined simply in terms of the absence of disease.
Second in the holistic theory:
1. Health is defined in terms of a person's ability to realise *his or her* vital goals.
2. Disease and other negative medical concepts are defined in terms of such states as are probable reducers of health (defined in the holistic way). (Nordenfelt, 1993B, p.281)

These then are the two principal elements which have been influential in the conceptualisation of health over many centuries, but neither provides an entirely satisfactory definition on its own; and the present purpose is not to criticise the two theories in detail, but simply to highlight some of the central concerns with each of them. In respect of the biostatistical theory, health is not defined in its own right, but merely as the absence of disease. So, much of the essence of the idea of health seems to disappear, becoming a negative, reductive and overly-restricted notion in which there is no room for the expression of either personal or social values. Part of the problem is that the concepts of health and disease are dissimilar in kind, so that as Ladd indicates 'Perhaps the crucial difference between health and disease is categorical, for health is a dispositional property (capacity or power), whereas disease is an occurrent property' (Ladd, 1988, p.277). Hence attempting to reduce health to no more than a lack of disease is logically mistaken. By way of contrast in the holistic theory, health becomes so general, abstract and open-ended, that whilst it captures the positive and evaluative qualities involved, it tends at the same time to be vacuous and so, difficult to put into practice. This is well illustrated by the famous WHO definition of health as 'a state of complete physical, mental and social well-being and not merely the absence of disease or infirmity' (World Health Organisation, 1948). Such efforts to conceptualise health in the abstract, without some reference to either illness or disease, which have a more substantial quality, must inevitably give rise to this kind of problem.

So neither of these two strands in the conceptualisation of health stands up well to scrutiny when analysed in isolation. However, as Dubos observes 'In one form or another these two complementary aspects of medicine have always existed simultaneously in all civilizations' (Dubos, 1960, p.131). Some combination of the two approaches may then be more satisfactory than either alone, although certain characteristics of each appear incompatible, e.g. reductionism and holism. Hence this route does not hold out the hope of discovering a unitary and unproblematic concept of health, and perhaps an important first conclusion is to accept that no such concept is or ever could be available. From which it follows that it is fruitless to seek such a holy grail.

A lack of health may at times be described in terms of illness and on other occasions of disease. What then is the difference between the two concepts of illness and disease? Clearly they are closely related, and in everyday language are often used interchangeably. Also in certain European languages, e.g. Polish, there is only a single word covering the English for both illness and disease. Nevertheless an important distinction is usually made between illness and disease, representing the difference between 'subjective' and 'objective' accounts produced from lay and professional perspectives respectively:

.... illnesses are *experiences* of discontinuities in states of being and in social role performance; diseases, in the scientific paradigm of modern medicine, are *abnormalities* in the *structure* and *function* of body organs and systems. (Eisenberg, 1976, p.5)

It follows that illness can occur without disease and vice versa, so that there is no necessary coincidence between them, as Eisenberg goes on to show in this example:

... the person with hypertension may be asymptomatic and therefore unconcerned when the physician who measures his blood pressure becomes alarmed; he may stop taking the prescribed medication because it makes

74

him 'ill', even though he is told it will mitigate his 'disease'. Only when the hypertension leads to congestive failure or hemiplegia will the person become a patient and agree with his doctor that he is sick: even then the agreement may be limited to a common perception that a *problem* exists which each is likely to formulate in quite different terms. (Eisenberg, 1976, p.5)

Whether the primary focus is on the concept of illness or disease will then have far-reaching consequences. If illness is taken as primary, personal suffering and care will claim the greatest attention, while if disease is emphasised over illness the process of diagnosis and cure is given primacy, and may become seen as an end in itself. As Cassell observes '... if disease and illness are not the same, curing and healing may well be very different functions; and what is good policy for one may not be good policy for the other' (Cassell, 1976, p.27).

Thus the concepts of illness and disease though clearly allied represent contrasting viewpoints which cannot be readily harmonised. It is difficult if not impossible to give comparable attention and weight to both of them, so that to concentrate on either is in part to deny the validity of the other. Equally, whichever is favoured will colour the way in which the concept of health is seen.

So it is apparent that it is difficult to separate out and focus on one of the three concepts of health, illness and disease in isolation, without at the same time making some reference to the others. This is because within the overall field of medicine and health care they represent a totality of related ideas which are interactive and so are not readily disentangled without misrepresentation, though for analytic purposes it may be necessary to focus on one at a time.

Turning then to this more comprehensive joint understanding of all three concepts what can be shown is that during the past two hundred years orthodox western medicine has developed so as to produce an imbalance between the two poles represented by Hygeian and Asclepian notions of health, illness and disease, with the last of these assuming a dominant role. The historical reasons for the development of this imbalance can be traced back to the Renaissance, and a clear demonstration of the changes that have occurred since then can be seen in the gradual decline in influence of humoral theory and its final demise in the nineteenth century, with the concomitant rise of biomedical theory. A number of philosophical aspects can be discerned in relation to this process and three will be focused on here because of their enduring relevance to present-day debates. These are the contrasts between nominalism and realism, normativism and positivism, and physiological and ontological accounts of disease. In very general terms nominalism, normativism and physiological accounts of disease form a cluster of ideas which have associations with Hygeia, whilst realism, positivism and ontological accounts of disease have associations with Asclepius.

The metaphysical distinction between nominalism and realism has been described in relation to disease by King. First nominalism:

> Attention to the individual as a concrete thing, makes up the doctrine of Nominalism. According to this view, relations, patterns, and qualities are only derivative. We call them abstractions. ... in the field of medicine, Mr Smith may have diabetes and Mr Jones hypertension. Then Smith and Jones are real, while diabetes and hypertension as abstractions are not real in the same sense. This view is summed up in the familiar expression, 'In "reality" there are no diseases, there are only sick patients'. (King, 1954, pp.200-201)

Second realism (in the Platonic tradition):

> The reality of a thing would consist, not in its concrete individuality but in the Forms or Universals which it exhibits. Particulars come into being and pass away, but the Universal qualities or Forms persist. According to this doctrine, diabetes and pneumonia would be Real, while any particular diabetic, like Mr Smith, merely manifests the disease ... diabetes, according to this view, is a real entity. (King, 1954, p.201)

The second distinction to be drawn is that between normativism and positivism, which like nominalism and realism are general philosophical terms which can be applied to disease. From the perspective of normativism the designation of disease is a process containing three main elements. First, that a particular state or condition of a person is judged abnormal; second that such an abnormality is judged to be a disease; and third that an explanation is offered for these judgements (all these judgements being evaluative rather than empirical). On the other hand a positivist view of disease contains the following elements. First that diseases are defined by reference to facts which are regarded as naturally determined; and second that, even when admitted, values are regarded as secondary to facts and do not play a part in the process of disease designation.

The final distinction is that between physiological and ontological views which are limited to a concern with disease and are portrayed by Cassell as follows:

> ... the physiological conception of disease, was embraced by the Hippocratic school which saw the origins of disease in an imbalance between the forces of nature within and outside the sick person. The second viewpoint, the ontological conception of disease, understands diseases to be

*entities*, things that invade and are localized in parts of the body. (Cassell, 1991, p.4)

When seen in general terms the ontological view of disease represents a particular example of realism, whereas the physiological view has no such direct relationship with nominalism.

What can be seen from these brief descriptions is that the ideas contained in realism, positivism and an ontological account of disease are closely allied and collectively present a coherent perception concerning the concepts of health, illness and disease, which has come to predominate in orthodox medicine in the west and underpins the biomedical model. The alternative ideas contained in nominalism, normativism and physiological accounts of disease, although less clearly related, are nevertheless all applicable to those alternative theories, such as humoral theory, which contrast with biomedicine.

From a western vantage, humoral theory and biomedical theory are the clearest and most important examples of how these two sets of ideas are associated symbolically with Hygeia and Asclepius respectively, and they demonstrate a different approach to all aspects of health, illness and disease. Some of the main contrasting features are shown in table 1.

It must be emphasised that it is not that humoral theory can be wholly identified with Hygeia, and biomedical theory with Asclepius (so for example current ideas about disease immunity are essentially Hygeian, though they are readily accommodated within biomedical theory), and in any case the theories are not operationalised in a pure form in practice. Nevertheless the switch from the dominance of humoral theory, which prevailed from Galen's time (2nd Century A.D.) until the eighteenth century, to biomedical theory which attained its purest expression and gained its greatest acclaim at the end of the nineteenth century and continues to predominate in a modified form, represented a very real and major shift in thinking about the concepts of health illness and disease.

The changes involved took place over a considerable timespan, and Jewson identifies the period from 1770-1870 as being of greatest significance (Jewson, 1976). He highlights the major implications for the roles and relationships of doctors and patients, and particularly emphasises how, as medical attention became increasingly disease orientated, the patients' accounts of their own illness experiences as a source of accepted medical knowledge have effectively disappeared. Foucault identifies a more dramatic change representing an important stage in this process, which occurred in the Paris hospitals, and heralded a new pathological era. In the *Birth of the Clinic* he claims that the publication of Bichat's work *Anatomie Générale* in 1801 marked a watershed: '... the great break in the history of western medicine dates precisely from the moment clinical experience became the anatomo-

Table 1

| Humoral Theory | Biomedical Theory |
|---|---|
| The primary focus is on a positive account of health, and on illness. | The primary focus is on disease as a discrete clinical entity. |
| The secondary focus is on disease in 'physiological' or ecological terms. | The secondary focus is a negative account of health as the absence of disease, and illness as an imperfect account of disease. |
| Disease is a manifestation of a lack of harmony or wholeness. | Disease represents a deviation from normal functioning. |
| Diseases are infinitely variable, reflecting the individuality of each patient. | Diseases are uniform and finite in number; hence there is a universal disease taxonomy, potentially identifiable without reference to particular patients. |
| The order of importance in the therapeutic process is as follows: (i) dietetics (a broad concept concerned with six aspects of how to lead a healthy life); (ii) medication; (iii) surgery. | The order of importance in the therapeutic process is as follows: (i) medication and surgery; (ii) prevention of disease; (iii) positive aspects of health and hygiene. |

clinical gaze' (Foucault, 1973, p.146).

These authors, then, draw attention to two important elements which were to form part of the emerging biomedical model which was completed in the second half of the nineteenth century, through the discovery and new understanding of micro-organisms as *the specific* cause of infectious diseases. The structure of this disease model was finally codified by Koch whose postulates were first published in 1891, and stated that:

first, the organism is always found with the disease, in accord with the lesions and clinical stage observed; second, the organism is not found with any other disease; third, the organism, isolated from one who has the disease and cultured through several generations, produces the disease [in a susceptible experimental animal]. (Koch, 1891, quoted in Susser, 1973, pp.22-23)

This was an extreme expression of the Asclepian notion, enshrining realist, positivist and ontological views of disease as paramount, and relegating the concepts of health and illness to subsidiary roles, entirely dependent on the prior definition of disease. As early as 1895, Virchow identified the logical fallacy in this model as it entailed a 'hopeless, never-ending confusion, in which the ideas of being (*ens morbi*) and causation (*causa morbi*) have been arbitrarily thrown together' (Virchow, 1895, translated by Rather, 1958, p.192). However Virchow himself was a thoroughgoing ontologist, who rather than challenging the underlying structure of this model, wished only to emphasise a different element, cellular pathology, as the primary defining feature.

A serious difficulty is now apparent with the contemporary over-emphasis on Asclepian notions at the expense of Hygeian ones. By starting from a primary focus on a particular account of disease, the concepts of health and illness become interpreted in a manner which by definition does no more than reflect the prior disease conception. So health and illness are not only relegated to a secondary position, but have no independent role. Equally, although the current concern is with Asclepian dominance, a similar problem would arise were the Hygeian notion to become predominant. In that case a particular description of health and illness would form the template, and the concept of disease would be shaped by it and so assume an inferior status.

The problem is that once one dispenses with the idea that the concepts of health, illness and disease can be fitted into a hierarchical structure, it is essential not to abstract and visualise one concept at a time without reference to the others, but to view them as forming an interactive network. However, as already shown, the many possible interpretations of each of the concepts are not all compatible, and so cannot be harmonised within a single framework. Hence if any progress is to be possible a start has to be made somewhere, but how might this be possible?

Two indications of how to approach this question may be of help. The first is to acknowledge the fruitlessness of seeking absolute and unitary definitions of the concepts, and to concentrate instead on searching for formulations of them that can be judged better than those which are presently accepted in both theory and practice. The second is to focus on the real development and use of the concepts in theory and practice, rather than more abstract accounts.

Bearing these points in mind it makes sense to begin by appraising the most extreme and pure expression of the biomedical model, described earlier, because it has formed the bedrock of conceptual thinking in medicine and health care for more than a century. Perhaps the most striking and controversial feature of that model is that all medical knowledge, including the concepts of health, illness and disease, is taken to be factual in nature and so value-free; or in a slightly modified version, that the essence and core of

79

the model is value-free, with value-laden knowledge being accepted but only as peripheral to the main medical enterprise. Boorse has developed his own particular philosophical defence of this latter position, which is widely acknowledged and frequently debated (Boorse, 1975). In praising the earlier work of Daly King, Boorse states:

> The root idea of this account is that the normal is the natural. The state of an organism is theoretically healthy, i.e., free of disease, insofar as its mode of functioning conforms to the natural design of that kind of organism. (Boorse 1975, p.57)

Using this assumption Boorse then develops his theoretical position with the claim that the concepts of health and disease are factually determined and value-free, whilst the concept of illness is value-laden but is dependent upon the concept of disease. The main features of the concepts of health, illness and disease which follow from this are that:

(a) Health is defined as the absence of disease, and is a normal state representing species typical functioning related to individual survival and reproduction.

(b) Disease is an impairment of normal functional ability.

(c) Illness relates to incapacity and is a subclass of disease.

For Boorse health and disease are the central concepts in medicine which complement one another by definition, and are derived from an objective account of medical science appropriately described and delineated by health care professionals. Hence there is no room for a more independent and positive account of health which is not tied to that of disease. Further patients' subjective accounts of their experience of illness have no independent validity, and represent only imperfect reflections of disease. Thus the concept of health is subservient to that of disease, and the concept of illness is subservient to both of them.

A wide range of criticisms have been made in response to Boorse by those who espouse a contrasting theoretical approach which stresses that the concepts of health and disease (as well as illness) are necessarily value-laden (see for example Engelhardt Jr., 1982). Some of the criticisms include that:

(a) The purpose and goals of man cannot be described in terms of a natural design.

(b) The concepts of health and disease cannot be adequately captured in biological and statistical terms which are themselves mechanical and reductionist.

(c) Describing disease as the key concept, and diseases as discrete entities, distorts and diminishes the concept and role of health.

(d) Describing illness as a subclass of disease denies the validity of the social construction of illness.

Two opposing sets of discourses have therefore been developed, the first relying on a positivist account of medicine as science, whereas the second derives from a normativist account involving social evaluation and explanation. In more practical terms the former emphasises diseases and their designation and treatment by doctors, whilst the latter focuses on patients, their experience of illness and their care.

In the late twentieth century few of those involved in health care still consider it right to adhere to a strict biomedical model, such as would be endorsed by Boorse's theoretical framework, but the question is how far they think it proper and are prepared to go in embracing the alternative normativist account. Most health care practitioners are willing to expand their conceptual understanding to allow for the relevance of the patient's interpretation of their illness experience; the complexities of social and psychological as well as biological factors in the aetiology of disease; and a less constricted and more positive account of health. But against this many of them are also concerned about what they see as the potential dangers associated with accepting the more open-ended and value-laden alternative models which derive from normativism. Three issues which are often raised are:

(a) That medicine will lose its proper and exclusive foundations, and thus health care professionals will sacrifice their claim to legitimacy.

(b) That the boundaries of medicine, medical work and health care policy will become unclear and confused.

(c) That the reassuring certainty of distinct professional and patient roles will be lost.

The theme that underlies all these issues is how to determine the extent and proper limits of medicine and so also of medical models and the concepts of health, illness and disease which inform them. Although this concerns the whole of medicine and health care the area which has probably been most contentious and widely debated is that of madness and the role of psychiatry, and so consideration of some of the central points which have been at issue here may help to throw light on the question more generally.

Szasz is perhaps the best known and most radical of the anti-psychiatrists, who takes an extreme and uncompromising positivist view of medical knowledge from which he claims that mental illness (which he conflates with mental disease) is a myth (Szasz, 1961). So he concludes that the category of behaviour that constitutes madness is improperly included within medicine, and that psychiatry as part of medicine is a bogus discipline. His starting point relies on the assumption that physical diseases are correctly regarded as medical because they can be described in terms of biological aetiology and abnormalities, and that by comparison most conditions which are presently designated as mental illnesses or diseases do not conform to these criteria.

However from a normativist perspective this assumption as to the legitimacy of physical disease described solely in biomedical terms is itself called into question, as shown in this quotation from Sedgwick:

> ... the anti-psychiatric critics themselves are wrong when they imagine physical medicine to be essentially different in its logic from psychiatry. A diagnosis of diabetes, or paresis, includes the recognition of norms or values. Anti-psychiatry can only operate by positing a mechanical and inaccurate model of physical illness and its medical diagnosis. It follows, therefore, from the above train of argument that mental illness can be conceptualised within the disease framework just as easily as physical maladies such as lumbago or TB. (Sedgwick, 1982, p.38)

He therefore concludes that:

> *All* illness, whether conceived in localised bodily terms or within a larger view of human functioning, expresses both a social value judgement (contrasting a person's condition with certain understood and accepted norms) and an attempt at explanation (with a view to controlling the disvalued condition). (Sedgwick, 1982, p.38)

Szasz's claim as a physicalist that his is the only way to provide a clear and legitimate boundary by which to delineate medicine and medical work through the exclusion of values appears then to be false, and its apparent strength in relieving uncertainty as to the limits of medicine is spurious. Bentall has shown that far from producing a precise and restrictive definition of medicine as suggested by Szasz, positivism could equally be used to sanction almost anything as falling within the medical sphere. He illustrated this in a 'spoof' article in which he set out to demonstrate that from a positivist perspective it would be logically possible to regard 'happiness' as a disease (Bentall, 1992). The point he wished to show was that because positivists deny that values have a role in the designation of disease, but in practice they cannot be excluded, they open up the potential for a whole range of different values to be smuggled in covertly. The question then is which particular values are being held by particular positivists, and in Szasz's case they reflect his radical libertarian views which are underpinned by his favouring a physicalist definition of illness and disease.

So it transpires that despite their claims to the contrary, positivists as well as normativists are reliant on values in determining what they consider to be the appropriate limits to medicine, and in constructing the medical models from which to derive those limits. As already indicated most people involved with medicine and health care no longer espouse a strict biomedical model and its attendant values, but ascribe instead to the biopsychosocial model, which has a more complex structure allowing for the inclusion of psychological and social elements as both causal factors and manifestations of disease. How far this indicates the recognition of a place for values, and the extent of their role, depends though on the interpretation of the model, and a number of different views are possible.

In the first of these the biopsychosocial model may continue to be seen in positivist terms, as simply an extension of the biomedical model. This would allow a place for psychological and social factors, but only as variables to be quantified and assessed in the same mechanical and reductionist way as biological variables have been previously. Thus although the field of medicine becomes enlarged, this is because of the incorporation of a greater range of facts rather than the acceptance of a role for values. Thus in conceptual terms little has been changed, other than the expansion of the medical sphere.

A second way of viewing the biopsychosocial model is to divide medicine into two parts, scientific and humanist (Wulff, 1990). The former then relates to acute medical conditions which continue to be seen in terms of positivism, whilst the latter relates to chronic conditions which require a different kind of understanding in terms of value-laden knowledge. The problem with this approach though is that acute conditions, which tend to be seen as the essential core of medicine, are left untouched by the change of model.

In a later article Wulff (1994) appears to embrace a different approach to the biopsychosocial model so introducing a third way of viewing it. This envisages the biological, psychological and social elements as being part of a more open system in which these different elements are interactive. The model may then be described in terms of general systems theory as follows:

According to this view *man represents an open system, which interacts sociophysically with the environment.* The system comprises physical processes, causally determined and willed mental processes, as well as psychosomatic and somatopsychic processes, and it interacts with the environment in the following two ways: 1) social interaction with other people and 2) physical interaction with the living and lifeless environment. (Wulff, 1994, p.18)

Engel spells out what he considers to be the requirements of a new medical model based on this theory. It would:

1. Allow for variability in the clinical expression of disease.
2. Be a scientifically rational approach to behavioral and psychosocial data.
3. Produce psychophysiologic responses to life change that may interact with existing somatic factors to alter susceptibility and thereby influence the time of onset, the severity and the course of a disease.
4. Allow for the fact that biochemical defect does not necessarily determine when the person falls ill or accepts the sick role, or status of patient.
5. Accept that 'rational' medical treatment may not restore the patient to health, even though the biochemical abnormality is corrected.
6. Acknowledge that the doctor/patient relationship has a powerful influence on the therapeutic encounter. (Engel, 1977, pp.131-132)

Whilst acknowledging that more sophisticated models such as are being suggested here can both incorporate values and allow for a fuller expression of Hygeian ideas, there is a danger that they may be seen as offering a new route to the holy grail of an absolute and unitary understanding of medicine and health care which was rejected earlier. No medical model or its related concepts of health, illness and disease can provide a definitive answer as to the precise limits to medicine, or to the exact way in which health care is properly to be understood, because ultimately they all depend on man's goals and values and these are always contested. Thus Dubos describes health as a mirage which can never be completely grasped or comprehended because it arises from a compound of the ever-changing complexity of man's physical body allied to the diversity of human goals and values (Dubos, 1960).

This should not lead though to the sceptical conclusion that all medical models and the concepts of health, illness and disease which relate to them are equally acceptable. All systems of medicine contain a balance between Hygeia and Asclepius, and the comparatively recent over-emphasis on the latter expressed through a positivist conception of medicine, is a historical aberration which requires correction. It produces a distorted image of disease as the paramount concept, which leads to a negative and somewhat empty conception of health, and also denies independent validity to a social conception of illness and suffering. In order to restore the balance all three concepts of health, illness and disease need to be considered jointly in an effort to determine a new relationship between them, which goes beyond merely replacing one set of ideas with another. This is part of the unending task of striving for a better vantage point with the real possibility of making progress, but without the false hope of reaching any final goal.


**Bibliography**

Bentall, R. (1992), 'A proposal to classify happiness as a psychiatric disorder', *Journal of Medical Ethics*, Vol. 18, pp.94-98.

Boorse, C. (1975), 'On the distinction between disease and illness', *Philosophy and Public Affairs*, Vol. 5, pp.49-68.

Caplan, A.L., Engelhardt Jr., H.T., and McCartney, J.J. (eds) (1981), *Concepts of Health and Disease*, Addison Wesley Publishing Co., London.

Cassell, E.J. (1976), 'Illness and disease', *Hastings Center Report*, Vol. 6, pp.27-37.

Cassell, E.J. (1991), *The Nature of Suffering and the Goals of Medicine*, Oxford University Press, New York and Oxford.

Dubos, R. (1960), *Mirage of Health*, George Allen and Unwin Ltd., London.

Eisenberg, L. (1976), 'Delineation of clinical conditions: conceptual models of 'physical' and mental disorders', in CIBA Foundation, *Research and Medical Practice: Their Interaction*, Elsevier, Amsterdam, pp.3-23.

Engel, G. (1977), 'The need for a new medical model: a challenge for biomedicine', *Science*, Vol. 196, pp.129-136.

Engelhardt Jr., H.T. (1975), 'The concepts of health and disease', in Engelhardt Jr., H.T. and Spicker, S. (eds), *Evaluation and Explanation in the Biomedical Sciences*, Reidel, Dordrecht, pp.125-141.

Engelhardt Jr., H.T. (1982), 'The roles of values in the discovery of illnesses, diseases and disorders', in Beauchamp, T.L. and Walters, L. (eds), *Contemporary Issues in Bioethics*, 2nd Edition, Wadsworth Publishing Company, Belmont, California, pp.73-5.

Foucault, M. (1973), *The Birth of the Clinic*, Tavistock, London (First published in French, 1963).

Jewson, N.D. (1976), 'The disappearance of the sick-man from medical cosmology, 1770-1870', *Sociology*, Vol. 10, pp.225-244.

King, L. (1954), 'What is disease?', *Philosophy of Science*, Vol. 21, pp.193-203.

Koch, R. (1891), 'Ueber Bakteriologische Forschung', in *Verhandlungen des X. Internationalen Medicinischen Congresses Berlin, 4-9 August 1890*, Hirschwald, Berlin (quoted in Susser, M. (1973), *Causal Thinking in the Health Sciences*, Oxford University Press, New York).

Ladd, J. (1988), 'The concepts of health and disease and their ethical implications', in Edwards, R.B. and Graber, G.C. (eds), *Bio-ethics*, Harcourt Brace Jovanovich, San Diego, pp.275-281.

Miller Brown, W. (1985), 'On defining 'disease'', *Journal of Medicine and Philosophy*, Vol. 10, pp.311-328.

Nietzsche, F.W. quoted in Downie, R.S. (ed.) (1994), *The Healing Arts*, Oxford University Press, Oxford (translated from the German by W. Kaufmann).

Nordenfelt, L. (1993A), 'On the relevance and importance of the notion of disease', *Theoretical Medicine*, Vol. 14, pp.15-26.

Nordenfelt, L. (1993B), 'Concepts of health and their consequences for health care', *Theoretical Medicine*, Vol. 14, pp.277-285.

Sedgwick, P. (1982), *Psycho Politics*, Pluto, London.

Szasz, T. (1961), *The Myth of Mental Illness*, Harper and Row, New York.

Virchow, R. (1895), 'One Hundred Years of General Pathology', originally published in German (translated by Rather, L.J. (1958), *Disease, Life and Man*, Stanford University Press, Stanford).

World Health Organisation (1948), 'Text of the Constitution of the World Health Organisation', *Official Records of the World Health Organisation*, Vol. 2, p.100.

Wulff, H. (1990), 'Function and value of medical knowledge in modern diseases', in ten Have, H.A.M.J., Kimsma, G.K., and Spicker, S.F. (eds), *The Growth of Medical Knowledge*, Kluwer Academic Publishers, Dordrecht, pp.75-86.

Wulff, H. (1994), 'The disease concept and the medical view of man', in Querido, A. (ed.), *The Discipline of Medicine*, Elsevier Science Publishers, Amsterdam, pp.11-19.

# 6 The nature of mental illness

*Neil Pickering*

In *Tell Me I'm Here* (Deveson, 1992) Anne Deveson tells the story of her son, Jonathan. From his late teens, and throughout the rest of his short life, Jonathan is said to suffer from schizophrenia. In one episode, for instance, Jonathan returns to the family home one night, and having threatened his mother (or perhaps himself) with a knife, is later found banging his head against the wall, speaking a strange mixture of gibberish and heart-breaking truth ('I'm mad Anne, Noddy Noddy'). His mother tries to get him admitted to hospital, and finally calls the police when all else fails. It is only her desperation which at last persuades them to put pressure on him to agree to be taken to a hospital (Deveson, 1992, pp.85-88).

Deveson's narrative is not only a description of a clinically recognised condition. It is also the story of a son, a mother, a family, friends and acquaintances, the police, the judiciary, psychiatrists, and alternative therapists, social workers, nurses, and members of the community of the mentally ill. It is, in short, the story not only of one person's mental illness, but also of the reactions and responses, beliefs, attitudes and values, ambiguous and variable, of individuals in a community, caught up in their various ways with the life of the central figure.

The question which this chapter seeks to explore is: 'What is the nature of mental illness (or disorder)?' (I shall assume that 'disorder' means the same as 'illness' and indeed 'disease' in what follows.) Deveson's account sets this question in a human and evaluative context. But what is the importance of such a context to any notion of mental illness? And does the notion of mental illness have any place at all within society?

The chapter starts with a consideration of two approaches to mental illness which differ with respect to their attitude to context, the individual, and the condition. The main aims will be furthered by an exploraton of a definition of mental illness which attempts to combine these two approaches to context.

I have in mind the definition of mental disorder recently advanced by Jerome C. Wakefield.

## The role of context

There are at least two approaches to investigating the nature of mental illness. One is to focus on the individual in the context in which he or she lives; another is to focus on the illness he or she has. As a contentious assertion, someone might say that psychiatric medicine takes the latter approach.

This statement needs qualifying. As a clinician charged with caring for a person such as Jonathan, the psychiatrist (like the psychiatric nurse and other health workers) is concerned with him as an individual. But, as a natural scientist, the psychiatrist is typically interested in the normal and abnormal functionings or structures of the human body or mind. From this point of view, the individual human is always an example of something (e.g. schizophrenia) which is said to be common to (or instanced in) each of a group of individual people. What is common to these people may be said to be common within and indeed across societies, cultures and time periods. Such specific contexts are transcended by the kind of normality and abnormality in which psychiatric medicine as a natural science finds its bearings.

The natural science approach can be contrasted with the approach of a sociologist, or historian, for example. The emphasis of natural science is on human biology, that which is shaped by natural processes, rather than on human social, cultural organisation, which is shaped by human belief, attitudes, and values. Jonathan might be approached in either way, and someone may suggest that the approaches complement one another.

## Wakefield's combined approach

Jerome C. Wakefield sums up his definition of all disorder (including mental disorder) as 'harmful dysfunction' (Wakefield, 1992A and 1992B). 'Harmfulness' is intended to be the social and cultural aspect, 'dysfunction' the biological medical aspect. Any individual who has a condition that harms her and is a dysfunction will (according to Wakefield) properly be said to be disordered.

Two things stand out about the definition. First, it proposes an answer to the question this chapter addresses, i.e. 'what is the nature of mental illness (or disorder)?'; and second it tries to combine the insights of psychiatric medicine into the biological (non-contextual) aspects of mental disorder, with an awareness of a more contextually sensitive human dimension. Wakefield himself describes the result as 'hybrid' (Wakefield, 1992A, p.374).

How is harm contextual? In this way: whether some condition of a person's mind, for instance, is or leads to a harm, is a matter of the value which may be placed upon it or upon what it leads to. And, it may be argued, many, if not all such judgements of value originate in, are learned from, and may indeed characterise particular societies and cultures at particular times. That is, judgements of what will count as harmful are related to the individual's context.

In contrast, non-evaluative or value-free ideas are supposedly attached to the aspect of dysfunction. That is to say, Wakefield claims that his account of dysfunction is independent of human evaluation or judgement (independent, then, of the human context). It is, rather, a matter of fact, contained now, or potentially, in the corpus of natural scientific knowledge about the human being.

Wakefield includes both aspects in his account of mental disorder, rather than turning to an entirely dysfunction-based (non-evaluative) or entirely harm-based (evaluative) account. He suggests that counter-examples are available to definitions of disorder which rest entirely on one or other of these. If disorder were the same as dysfunction then, Wakefield claims, explanting kidneys from living donors would be equivalent to giving the donors a disorder, which is clearly not how it is generally thought of (Wakefield, 1992A, p.384). If disorder were any internally caused disvalued state (as Wakefield claims Sedgwick (1982) holds), then any harm caused by the person to herself would be a disorder. But, though it may be harmful (and is certainly disvalued) ignorance is not generally accounted a disorder (Wakefield, 1992A, p.376). Having both aspects seems necessary.

One question which may immediately arise from yoking together an evaluative and a non-evaluative aspect in the definition of disorder is what the relationship of the two can be. So far as I can see, Wakefield does not spend time on this point, but it is interesting to take it up as a way of exploring his ideas. It can be argued, first of all, that the relationship cannot be one merely of their co-existence in an individual. If it could be, then the joint presence of any dysfunction (say, lacking one kidney, to take up Wakefield's example) with any harm (say unemployment) would constitute a disorder. But this seems implausible.

However, the relationship between them cannot (for Wakefield's purposes) be definitional either. That is to say, for Wakefield the two aspects must be definable independently of one another. To show why this is, I will try imagining how someone might react, faced with Jonathan Deveson. Someone may feel intuitively that 'something has gone wrong' with him. This may be cashed out to suggest both an evaluation of his behaviours and something additional to that evaluation.

At first sight, what may be meant is that something other than his own will is making Jonathan act in the way he is.[1] That is to posit a 'something' that causes or strongly influences his behaviours. It is not clear what this something would be. Wakefield claims to be uninterested in whether the thing is brain structure abnormalities, brain chemistry imbalances, or something entirely mental. He claims that any of these would fit in with his account. As a causal agent, that 'something' would be describable independently of the behaviours themselves. The disvalued behaviours may be said to draw attention to this something, but that would be all.

However, what has just been described is not yet the right object for Wakefield's purposes. Certainly, if such a causal relationship could be established between Jonathan's self-harming behaviours (or his motivations, or attitudes) and that 'something', it would be reasonable to claim that a value-neutral biological discovery had been made. However, the matter-of-fact existence of a causal mechanism for a behaviour goes no distance towards showing that there is a dysfunction present. For example, behaviours (both harmful and beneficial) may be causally determined by instinct; and all that follows from this is that the instincts are functioning.

Perhaps, however, it is the causal link to a behaviour which is characteristically harmful which would entail that there is a dysfunction. For instance, depressive behaviours may be said to be disordered because a set of behaviours which are characteristically harmful to the person and which arise in the presence of an underlying causal entity, entail dysfunction. However, this would not do for Wakefield either. One reason for this is that, since Wakefield sees harms as evaluative, their mere presence in any definition of dysfunction will undermine its value-neutrality.

What, then, is the relationship of harmfulness to dysfunction in Wakefield's account? The previous arguments show the two cannot be linked definitionally. Their relationship must, then, be investigable empirically; but it cannot be a relationship of mere coexistence. The most plausible relationship of the two aspects of disorder will be one of dysfunction causing, or (perhaps more loosely) leading to, harm. These remarks can be construed as a way of emphasising the two different kinds of ideas within Wakefield's notion of disorder. Dysfunction, in Wakefield's view, comes from the value-free world of biology and medicine conceived of as a natural science. Harmfulness comes from the human world, and is tied up with human culture and attitudes.

Wakefield claims that his concept of mental disorder stands on the border between the biological and the social. It might be more correct to say that it stands with a foot in both realms.

## Physical and mental

Now, it is all very well to say that Wakefield's concept has a foot in both realms, but someone may observe that these two realms are very different from one another. Associated with this observation, there may appear now to be some problems for Wakefield's definition; and though some (at least) will turn out to rest upon a confusion, it is important to express them.

The confusion I have in mind underlies arguments such as the following. The world of biological facts, free of human values, is generally conceived of as a physical world, working in accordance with natural laws. Characteristically, however, the human ability to evaluate is connected to the abilities to think, to feel, and so on, all of them mental, and all of them linked to human contexts. So, it looks as if the contextualised and evaluative aspect of Wakefield's definition of disorder is connected to the human mind, while the value-free notion of dysfunction is connected to the body. But then, dysfunction will invariably be a physical thing. Consequently, mental dysfunction seems to be ruled out, and with it, mental disorder.

What is confused here? In fact, though the human mind is the source of evaluation, it may still be a biological creation, the result of evolution, perhaps describable in biological terms. Certainly, it may not be reducible to the physical. But, it may be argued, it still has functions, and perhaps, in some sense, structures (Wakefield, 1992A, p.378); and if the mind may have functions, it may have dysfunctions. The human mind then, may, at one and the same time, be the source of evaluation, and describable in value-free biological terms. Given Wakefield's account of disorder, and his belief that it may apply to the mental as well as the physical, he must assume this is the case. In the present section of this chapter, his assumption will be contested.

Those trying to explain the nature of mental illness may start with the notion of physical illness. So too may those engaged in a related debate about the reality of mental illness. The question at issue in this debate is: 'Is there any such thing as an illness of the mind at all?' Clearly, those on opposite sides in this debate would see Jonathan in very different terms. For those who believe that there is no such thing as mental illness, some other explanation of his behaviour and experiences will be appropriate. For those who believe that there is such a thing as mental illness, some explanation from among those available to psychiatrists will be relevant.

However, it is worth stopping to consider the actual terms of the debate about the reality of mental illness. Fulford, in a subtle analysis, suggests that some on quite opposite sides of this question set off apparently from the same starting point (but this is only an appearance, as will emerge soon). Fulford's analysis particularly concerns, on the one hand, Szasz, the celebrated anti-psychiatrist, and on the other, Kendell, an advocate of psychiatry (Fulford,

91

1989, pp.5-7). Fulford argues that, despite the fact that Szasz utterly denies the existence of mental illness, while Kendell enthusiastically embraces it, both start from the assumption that the paradigmatic case of disease or illness is physical disease or illness. Having simply assumed this, each argues to his conclusion. Their shared method of arguing, then, is to test the conceptual propriety of physical illness in the case of mental conditions. But what then, leads them to opposite conclusions?

Fulford argues that, in reality, each takes different features of physical illness to be primary. However, to take a wider point from his analysis, Fulford recognises that the propriety of extending the notion of illness to the mind from the body is at the heart of many disagreements about the nature and reality of mental illness. But is it appropriate to do so? Consider the following argument from a psychiatrist, attempting to show that there really is a thing called mental illness:

> Diabetes mellitus is analogous to Schizophrenia in many ways. Both are symptom clusters ... Each may have many etiologies and show a range of intensity from severe and debilitating to latent or borderline ... The medical model seems to be quite as appropriate for the one as for the other. (Kety, 1974, p.962, quoted in Szasz, 1987, p.150)

It is worth considering what exactly is being claimed here, and contrasting that with what can actually be claimed. Kety starts off with a condition - diabetes mellitus - which he assumes all will agree is a (physical) illness. He then takes a series of features of that physical illness, and points out that the same features can be found in another condition, schizophrenia. From this fact, he wants to conclude that both are rightly described in medical terminology.

Now, taken at face value, some of the argument here is patently circular. When Kety states that schizophrenia, like diabetes, is a 'cluster of symptoms', he is simply assuming the answer he is supposed to be proving. If schizophrenia has symptoms, then, clearly, it is already being described using the medical model. What remains to be shown is that the features of schizophrenia Kety has in mind are indeed symptoms.

However, Kety also uses less obviously medical language. He refers to severity, latency, and so on. His argument is that schizophrenia shows degrees of these; and, in this, it is like diabetes. The notion of severity in the condition begins to look like one genuine reason for thinking of it as being of the same kind as diabetes.

How strong a reason is it? One argument against it is that, so far, no justification has been given for thinking that severity of schizophrenia (or diabetes, for that matter) is part of what defines it as an illness. Unlike Wakefield's notions of harmfulness and dysfunction, severity, latency, and so on, may perhaps be true of some, but not all, illnesses or disorders. A further objection is that many different things show degrees of severity, from frost, to looks. It does not at all follow that these are illnesses. Severity, in different cases, may have different implications.

If this is true of the severity of frosts and looks, what is to prevent it being true of the severity of schizophrenia, such that the severity of diabetes, and the severity of schizophrenia, are different kinds of severity? The only thing weighing against this in the Kety passage, is the supposed conclusion of the argument; that is, that schizophrenia and diabetes are both rightly called illnesses. But then the argument from severity turns out to be circular, like that from symptoms.


### Literal and metaphorical

There is still a puzzle, however. Kety, after all, does (on the face of it) use these terms to talk about schizophrenia, and, moreover, the vast majority of people would probably be inclined to talk in the same way. But if Szasz is right that there is no such thing as mental illness, how could this way of talking be so pervasive and persuasive? Szasz's explanation is that the language of medicine, disorder, and so forth, when applied to mental conditions, is metaphorical.

Szasz's claim is this: so far as symptom, severity, latency, and so forth, are concerned, the likenesses they seem to suggest between schizophrenia and diabetes are metaphorical likenesses. Now, typically metaphors are thought of as a form of likening. But the point about likenesses which may be drawn to attention in a metaphor, is that they are not literal likenesses.

The distinction intended here may be cashed out as follows. A literal likeness refers to some quality or feature which is actually present in both of two objects. For instance, a book and a football may literally be like each other. Each may be red, for example. When it comes to the features of an object that make it a book, then these may be things such as pages, perhaps with writing on them, perhaps in some form of binding, and so on. Anything which literally has pages with writing on them in some form of binding will then have a fair claim actually to be a book.

But something which has pages metaphorically will not be classed as a book, except metaphorically. For instance, I may describe my memory as having pages, with what happened to me written on them, and as bound into my mind. It makes a kind of sense to say that memory is like a book; but the notion of like here is metaphorical. However many metaphorical likenesses may be found between books and memories - and they may be legion - they will never add one ounce of weight to the claim that memories really are books.

Szasz replies to Kety is this way:

> Note that Kety first analogizes somatic and psychological *symptom clusters* ... and then proceeds to treat them as if they were the same sorts of things. As a result he misinterprets what is meant by a metaphor, treating a metaphorical disease as a disease instead of as a metaphor. (Szasz, 1987, p.150)

This is a hypothesis. That is, Szasz's point is that if these likenesses (or analogies) are metaphorical, then the two things will not actually be of the same kind. We need still to be shown that these are metaphorical likenesses, as Szasz claims they must be. What can justify the contention that the use of medical, disease and illness terms in the case of, say, Jonathan Deveson, are metaphorical?


**Mental and physical**

To see the basis of the claim, attention must be focused on the concept 'mental' within mental illness. Szasz's contention is that the mind is not the sort of thing which can become literally ill. He argues to this conclusion in the following way. He notes, first, that disease is standardly defined by structural lesions and bodily dysfunctions (Szasz, 1987, pp.24-25) for which he is criticised by Wakefield (1992A, p.375). Human bodies have structures (organs and systems made out of cells) which may have lesions and may dysfunction. They, then, can have illnesses. But minds have structures and organs only metaphorically, at best. The mind is not literally a structure, and cannot literally dysfunction (any more than the memory can literally have pages with writing on them). The mind literally cannot be ill.

However, at this point, Fulford's argument (Fulford, 1989, pp.5-7) is worth recalling. He says that to get to their quite opposite conclusions, Szasz and Kendell take different accounts or aspects of physical disease to be primary. Szasz's assumption is that disease standardly means physical dysfunctioning. Not surprisingly, he can argue from this to his conclusion that there is no such thing as mental illness.

Wakefield appears to avoid Szasz's argument; but not, at first sight, by taking some other feature of physical disorder to be primary. Indeed, Wakefield is inclined to put aside the question of what can truly be said about the mental, as opposed to the physical, as a less contentious issue than what can truly be said about disorder (Wakefield, 1992B, p.233). He asserts that, when it comes to 'harmful dysfunction', the same set of concepts apply literally to both the physical and the mental (Wakefield, 1992A, p.375).

But he gives only light support to his assertion. He notes that Darwin thought the mind had functions, and that the mind plays a role in human survival and reproduction (like the body), and that evolution may explain the existence of both body and mind (Wakefield, 1992A, p.375). But none of these amounts to an argument, since it is not at all clear what must follow from any of these points. For instance, it was earlier argued that the fact that the mind is the source of evaluation does not show that it is not a result of evolution and that it may perhaps be biologically describable. However, were the mind the result of evolution it would not follow that it must be describable in terms which apply literally also to the body.

What, then, would convincingly show that Wakefield's assumption is good, while Szasz's is not?


## Functions and the mind

The biological part of Wakefield's account is a functional account. Any clues available as to how Jonathan's mind is working will be found largely in his behaviour and his talk. Some of this is bizarre, some threatening, some harmful to his mother, some harmful to himself. And, to recall an earlier point, some or all of it may give rise to the intuition that 'something has gone wrong' with Jonathan, where that intuition is to do both with the evaluation of his behaviours and the implication that some dysfunction is present.

Some idea of what functions may be imputed to the mind is necessary if a start is to be made on expanding the latter part of the intuition. Wakefield makes some suggestions as to what mental mechanisms (and hence functions) there may be, and he lists these as including 'cognitive, motivational, affective, personological, hedonic, linguistic, and behavioral dispositions and structures' (Wakefield, 1992A, p.375). He also notes that this is clearly a major area for further conceptual research (Wakefield, 1992B, p.246).

One mechanism Wakefield does not mention separately in this list is an 'evaluational' mechanism. Earlier in the chapter, evaluation was identified as something connected to the human mind, and to the context in which humans live, to society and culture, time and place. It can perhaps be supposed that some evaluation is present in behavioural, motivational and affective dispositions. It will prove to be important to recall the presence of evaluation in what follows, even if it is not given the rank of a function of the mind. A culturally and historically distinct example will be used to help answer the question as to how dysfunction may be found in behaviours and talk like Jonathan's, and to test the effectiveness of Wakefield's definition in identifying disorder and distinguishing it from other conditions.

The example concerns an American woman (Mrs E.P.W. Packard) who was committed to an asylum by her preacher husband after she had expressed religious views with which he disagreed (cf. Szasz, 1973, p.42, p.159). Mrs Packard, however, argued that:

> a person should not be committed as insane solely on the base of the opinions he might express and ... commitment should be based only on irregular conduct which indicates that the individual is so lost to reason as to render him an unaccountable moral agent. ('Mrs Packard's prison life', 1867, in Lindman and McIntyre, 1961, p.13, quoted in Greenland, 1970, p.12)

Mrs Packard's point is subtle. She is arguing that the only good reason for committing someone to an asylum is that she is 'lost to reason' in such a way that she is considered 'an unaccountable moral agent'. But she notes, also, that this 'unaccountability' must be found in her irregular conduct or her opinions (that is, it must be found in what is disvalued in her particular time and place).

To put Mrs Packard's point in Wakefieldian terms: she is insisting that she be declared mentally disordered if and only if a dysfunction is indicated in her disvalued behaviours - in her case unorthodox religious views. The question which may now be posed is this: would Wakefield's account free Mrs Packard from her committal, or would it validate it? And the point of the question is that if it would justify her committal, then it seems to justify a practice which probably appears quite unacceptable to readers today, by offering her husband the medical backing he needs to get her committed.

Wakefield, if trying to avoid this outcome, might first point out that Mrs Packard's opinions are not harmful to her; and since they are not, the question of whether they are caused by or (more loosely) associated with some dysfunction, is quite irrelevant. However, this reply misses the point of the example. Given a certain religious orthodoxy, it is quite plausible to say that having a particular opinion is harmful to the person who has it. Mrs Packard may have been committed 'for her own good' on the view that her mortal soul was in danger if she was not somehow freed of these heretical beliefs. They are harmful then; so, are they created by something other than her own will (suggesting a dysfunction)?

But here, Wakefield might seem to have a cunning response. If her beliefs are caused by something other than her own will, then they are not really her beliefs, and so could not harm her. If, on the other hand, they really are her beliefs, then they have not been caused by anything other than her own will, and so the question of dysfunction does not arise. In either case, on Wakefield's account, there is no disorder (though in the first case there may still be a dysfunction).[2]

However, cunning though this response is, it is not quite cunning enough.

The problem for Mrs Packard, from the orthodox point of view, is not necessarily that she is expressing heretical beliefs which she may not hold, but that she is not expressing those right thinking beliefs she does hold. The 'real' Mrs Packard may have disappeared; and for the good of that real Mrs Packard, she must be recovered. If she still expresses unorthodox views then, she must be given up. But surely some attempt must be made by psychiatry to get her back. To an asylum with her, then.

If this point is right, then Wakefield's account has run into some trouble. The trouble is that whether something is or is not a harm to someone may be a matter of contention between that someone and others. Mrs Packard may argue, for instance, that having her views is not a harm to her, even if she really does hold them, since her view is that the orthodoxy is wrong about the harmfulness of unorthodox views, as it is about much else.

Is there, then, a harm here or not? Since Wakefield's account of harmfulness does not specify who is to judge this matter, it is as likely to support Mrs Packard's committal as not. A way forward, however, may now seem clear for someone who takes Wakefield's position (though it is not clear that Wakefield himself would take it). It is this. If no dysfunction can be found which is *causally related* to Mrs Packard's beliefs, behaviours, or talk, then the harmfulness which arises cannot be the harmfulness of disorder, and she should not be committed.

Unfortunately, this way forward is not quite so useful as it at first may seem. The problem is that supposing it were found that there was indeed some thing (other than her own will) which was causing Mrs Packard's unorthodox beliefs, or was at least contributing largely to their existence, this dysfunction, to be proof of a disorder, must lead to or cause a harm to Mrs Packard. But, of course, that is precisely what she may deny. The point is that the mere presence of a dysfunction with a causal relationship to a behaviour, or even belief, is not enough to show disorder. The behaviour or belief must also be harmful. The presence or absence of dysfunction cannot adjudicate between different stories as to the harmfulness of some result of dysfunction. Mrs Packard's views cannot be harmful to her because they arise from a dysfunction of her mind; they can be harmful to her because and only because they are evaluated as such.

This seems to be a point favouring Wakefield's position, since it cuts off a justification for committing Mrs Packard which Reverend Packard might have been inclined to use. However, it does not oppose committal either. It merely states that some other justification than the presence of a causal dysfunction is necessary. But that other justification may start with the assertion that Mrs Packard's behaviour is harmful, which Wakefield's definition does not oppose.

## Function and evaluation

Nevertheless, Wakefield's account, with the addition of the causal relation of dysfunction to harm, should help Mrs Packard. If no dysfunction can be found, then she is clearly not disordered, and, however harmful her beliefs or behaviours may be to her (in the view of her husband and others), she should not be committed as insane. (Similar hopes might be held out over the debate about the classification of homosexuality.) But, the notion of dysfunction, if it was to be able to show that Mrs Packard was sane, would probably need to be free of those evaluative influences which, in the view of her society, made her a danger to herself. The value-freedom of the notion would ensure this, so for Wakefield's position, a good deal hangs on whether the notion of dysfunction is value-free.

The debate as to whether any idea of dysfunction can be value-free is clearly relevant here; but there is not space to consider it further. And nor, except impressionistically, is there space to consider whether any of the particular functions which Wakefield says exist in the mind, are literally describable free of values. What may be said, with regards to these, is the following.

Szasz might offer an account of human behaviours, beliefs, feelings, and so forth, which is factual, in one sense, but which, in another sense, undermines any account of the mind which purports to reduce its workings to biologically conceived mental functions. What he might do is to point out that all human behaviours, beliefs, feelings, and motivations, are bound up with human evaluation. To take Mrs Packard's case again, it can be said that her beliefs, and the behaviours which result from them and show them, imply values. These are the values she uses to judge her own acts, beliefs, and so on. Szasz might argue that any judgement that these values are harmful to her must be subject to two limitations. First, it must be shown that they really are harmful to her, which requires (for him) that she agrees they are. Second, and simultaneously, it must be the case that she does not will to act as she is acting. This, in turn, seems to require that it be shown at least that she is acting, or feeling, or believing, contrary to her own values. And this, from Szasz's perspective, may require, once again, her agreement that she is.

Someone may argue that certain sets of values are themselves evidence of, or caused by, dysfunction. But the claim is not sustainable, if the nature of dysfunction is to be value-free. This is because dysfunction in this case must be definitionally tied to an evaluation of the values themselves, which would render it value-laden. Someone might wonder if a dysfunction could be found independent of this judgement. However, it is difficult to assert that the evaluative function of the mind has gone wrong when it clearly is evaluating. And it must be admitted that it is evaluating, since it is precisely a harmful (a disvalued) evaluation which has raised a question about whether it is functioning or not.

For these reasons, someone taking Szasz's general line might reject altogether the idea that the essence of what the human mind does can be captured in a biological account of its functions, even presuming such functions could be identified. Everything the human mind does is bound up with the values the person holds. Mrs Packard, the argument goes, is always in some danger from Wakefield's account, since it ignores this fact about the human mind.


## Insight

Szasz might claim that only his account can meet contemporary intuitions that what happened to Mrs Packard was wrong. The argument for this has rested upon the importance which it places upon her evaluation of the harmfulness of her own behaviours. Without her agreement that they are harmful, Szasz might argue, it is quite wrong to declare that they are.

Moreover, to take this line of argument further, it is quite often the case that people who are labelled mentally disordered, deny that they are. If the same rule is to apply here as applies with the notion of harm, then the denial will be decisive here too. On this argument, then, no one can be mentally ill unless she agrees she is.

Where someone is said to be mentally ill, but denies it, then others often argue that she lacks insight. Now, for Szasz, the idea that someone lacks insight because she cannot see she is mentally ill, would be nonsensical. Since Szasz thinks there is no such thing as mental illness, the person who denies that she is mentally ill when all around her are saying she is really, is the only one who is showing any insight. However, by the same token, no one who says 'I am suffering from mental illness' can be showing insight either. For instance, suppose someone claims that she has obsessive urges to steal which she cannot resist though wanting to (the example is Flew's and his account is based upon Freud's; cf. Flew, 1975, pp.54-55). The insight here need not be framed as a psychiatric diagnosis; it need be only an intuition of the person him or herself that 'something has gone wrong' cashed out in the way it was cashed out earlier. Szasz would have to say that the person who says this of herself lacks insight. Although, in some cases, there may be good reasons for saying so, Szasz seems committed to saying there are always good and indeed decisive reasons for saying so.

If this extreme position is rejected, and it is allowed that sometimes someone may have a true insight that she is mentally disordered ('I'm mad, Anne'), what follows? Two things seem to. The first is that Szasz's position that there is no such thing as mental illness is flatly contradicted. Admittedly, the contradiction is based upon an intuition of a general nature, which is perhaps a minute first step. Even so, that seems to be more than Szasz is prepared to allow.

The second is that Wakefield's account seems a great number of steps further off. Before the intuition that 'something has gone wrong' can be explained in terms of 'harmful dysfunction' defined in the way Wakefield defines it, a good deal of argument is required. Not least, it has to be shown that Wakefield's claim that the notion of dysfunction is something definable in value free and biological terms, is both plausible, and applicable to the mind. As has been suggested in this chapter, showing this cannot be a straightforward task. Judgements of harmfulness must be evaluative and context dependent; but agreement over such judgements is potentially problematic, and this may affect the designation of someone as mentally ill.

This need not be a weakness of Wakefield's position. It may indeed have captured something about current views of someone who is said to have a condition such as schizophrenia, that they are various, and sometimes radically divergent from one another, as were the views of those who came into contact with Jonathan Deveson.

### Acknowledgement

I would like to acknowledge the help of Martyn Evans in the writing of this chapter.

### Notes

1.  Whether the will can be described as a cause of behaviour, or whether, indeed, there is any thing independent of behaviours, beliefs, attitudes and so on which could be called 'the will' is a matter for discussion.

2.  It looks as if we might want to say there is something wrong with her nonetheless, even though these expressions of belief could not harm her; Wakefield's account seems to prevent us doing so.

### Bibliography

Deveson, A. (1992), *Tell Me I'm Here*, Penguin, Harmondsworth.
Flew, A. (1975), *Crime or Disease?* Macmillan, London.

Fulford, K.W.M. (1989), *Moral Theory and Medical Practice*, Cambridge University Press, Cambridge.

Greenland, C. (1970), *Mental Illness and Civil Liberty*, Social Administration Research Trust, London.

Kety, S. (1974), 'From rationalisation to reason', *American Journal of Psychiatry*, 131, pp.957-963.

Lindman, F.T. and McIntyre, D.M. (eds) (1961), *The Mentally Disabled and the Law*, University of Chicago Press, Chicago.

Sedgwick, P. (1982), *Psycho Politics*, Harper and Row, New York.

Szasz, T. (1973) *The Manufacture of Madness. A Comparative Study of the Inquisition and the Mental Health Movement*, Paladin, St Albans.

Szasz, T. (1987), *Insanity. The Idea and its Consequences*, John Wiley and sons, New York.

Wakefield, J.C. (1992A), 'The concept of mental disorder. On the boundary between biological facts and social values', *American Psychologist*, Vol. 47, No. 3, pp.373-388.

Wakefield, J.C. (1992B), 'Disorder as harmful dysfunction: a conceptual critique of *DSM-III-R*'s definition of mental disorder', *Psychological Review*, Vol. 99, No. 2, pp.232-247.

# 7  Alternative, complementary, holistic …

*John Saunders*

I have laboured to the utmost of my power, if by any means it might be, that the cure of diseases may be managed after I am dead with greater certainty: for I esteem any progress in that kind of knowledge (how small so-ever it be) though it teach no more than the cure of the toothache or of corns upon the feet, to be of more value than the vain pomp of nice speculations. (Sydenham, 1668)

The computer database Medline defines alternative medicine as non-orthodox therapeutic systems which usually have no satisfactory scientific explanation for their effectiveness. Such a definition serves in a rough and ready way: though many advocates of alternative medicine claim the status of science even if a 'different science'. The World Health Organisation has defined alternative medicine as all forms of health care provision which usually 'lie outside the official health sector' (British Medical Association, 1993, p.5). 'Alternative medicine' was the title used in a seminal editorial in the British Medical Journal (Smith, 1983; cf. also Lister, 1983) as well as the title of the 1986 BMA report (Board of Science Working Party on Alternative Therapy, 1986). But 'alternative' is not really satisfactory. Indeed some 'alternative' authorities are quite insistent in rejecting the label: 'registered osteopaths do not offer alternative treatment' (General Council and Register of Oesteopaths, 1989, p.2). Unconventional approaches are additional or complementary to conventional Western medicine, not a substitute. To its opponents, of course, it isn't a real alternative anyway. For Baylis (1988, p.1459), 'complementary is the right word'. Most patients, he comments, use unconventional treatments to complement, rather than as alternative to, orthodox medicine. When seriously ill, they revert to orthodoxy. Of course, this may describe what people actually do but does not establish that such therapies or techniques are truly complementary i.e. that they do in fact add something of importance to the patient's progress or well being. Thus some critics do not accept the validity of this term either:

> 'Complementary' suggests that the intervention can augment, assist, or enhance the effect of a treatment already going on. Therapies that have not shown worth by objective standards are not truly 'complementary'. At best, they are 'unproven and untested'; at worst, they are fraudulent and quackery. (Monaco and Green, 1993, p.89)

The recent BMA report adopted the title 'complementary medicine', but used the phrase 'non-conventional' throughout. This too has been criticised, for if doctors do use alternative methods, this would seem to define them as conventional:

> Perhaps one way of defining non-conventional medicine is to consider the exact nature of conventional medicine. The 1858 Medical Act would seem to suggest 'that conventional medicine is any treatment delivered by a registered medical practitioner'. In some instances this might mean homoeopathy or acupuncture; consequently the definition of complementary medicine becomes confused. (Lewith, 1993, p.218)

Gevitz opted for the term 'sectarian medicine' (Gevitz, 1987), believing that this describes the deviant social status and social movement participation of its practitioners. The term is pejorative and has been used by dominant groups in religion to describe those who subscribe to false doctrine. More venerable and less abusive is 'fringe medicine', used by Brian Inglis as the title for a widely read book in 1964 (Inglis, 1964) - though he thought it a misnomer. He construed the basic distinction between orthodoxy and unorthodoxy to be professional organisation. Any doctor can employ methods commonly associated with the fringe, and almost every fringe method has some doctors using it or at least sympathetic to it. Inglis conceded that he could not discuss fringe treatments for individual disorder; or those designed for a special purpose, like Steinach's for rejuvenation or Professor Niehans' Cell therapy; or those claiming to be comprehensive yet without international standing (Alexander Technique, for example); or, commonest of all, folk medicine. Inglis classified the systems he described into those for the body (herbalism, homoeopathy), for the mind (hypnotherapy, psychotherapy) and the spirit (healing, radiesthesia) - a curiously reductionistic approach. Glymour and Stalker (1985) prefer the term 'holistic medicine'. For them this is a movement encompassing a vast number of exotic therapies and procedures: acupuncture, therapeutic touching, cancer therapy through visualisation, Rolfing, flower remedies, reflexology, homoeopathy, herbalism, chiropractic, aromatherapy, chelation therapy, colonics, macrobiotic diets, hair analysis, iridology, psychic diagnosis, polarity therapy and others. These procedures are holistic because they are endorsed in books on holistic medicine, and supported by organised associations: the American Holistic Medical Association, British Holistic Medical Association, Canadian Holistic Medical Association, American Holistic Nursing Association and so on. The holistic movement and the holistic associations stand for more than treating the 'whole person'. Most books on individual complementary practices claim holistic sympathies and holistic associations support or advocate complementary medicine. 'Holistic' may be used in the narrow sense of treating the 'whole person', but it also carries a wider meaning, referring to a number of ideals embraced by nonconventional practitioners.

While Inglis ignored the more bizarre fringe areas, Glymour and Stalker point out that the American Holistic Medical Association hasn't: its 1984 meeting apparently included lectures on Spiritual Attunement, Electromagnetic Man, Free Radical Pathology, Transpersonal Use of Imagery and Shamanism (Glymour and Stalker, 1985, p.11).

If the demarcation between science and non-science has generated a large debate among philosophers of science, the problems of demarcation in unconventional medical practice are even harder. On the one hand, there is difficulty classifying practices that are orthodox in one setting (e.g. hypnosis) but 'alternative' in another; and on the other hand in distinguishing well regulated, highly organised systems (e.g. homoeopathy, osteopathy), from the bizarre or fraudulent (or both). Henney (1993, p.86) quotes a FDA survey claiming that an estimated 38-40 million Americans try fraudulent remedies each year. Yet an issue of the *New York State Journal of Medicine* in 1993 dedicated to unproven therapy and quackery illustrated the problem of demarcation with an advertisement for the unproven sexual stimulant, yohimbine, (? orthodox) opposite its contents page at the start of the issue; and an advertisement for a practice in acupuncture (? alternative) after the last article at the end of the issue.

Pietroni (1992, p.564) argues that all terms in current use may describe dissimilar activities:

> The term 'alternative' or 'complementary' medicine is used as a catch all definition for anything not taught at a Western medical school. It is thus a definition by exclusion and as helpful a term as 'foreign.' An Englishman setting out to comment on 'foreigners' would be as accurate in his description of foreigners as most doctors are in their understanding of alternative therapies, and the Englishman's commentaries on foreigners would tell us more about the prejudices of being English than the characteristics of non-English people.

Of course, it might not always. He proposes a classification of alternative medicine into four areas: complete systems, diagnostic methods, therapeutic modalities and self care approaches. But it is still a subdivision of something. Behind the labels lies a desire to draw distinctions that have been difficult since at least the 18th century (cf. Bynum and Porter, 1987). Although an ideal term for alternative or holistic medicine may be impossible, it can be claimed that these terms (or most of their alternatives) embrace a loose coalition of practices with a number of common features that go beyond 'not taught in (British) medical schools'. Such practices also attract a particular constituency of public support, with links to 'green' and environmental issues. Essentialism - looking for a single defining feature - is not a productive approach. In discussing features of this loose coalition, there may be exceptions. The reader should not assume the issues discussed here apply to every therapy or technique, but ask whether they do.


**Historical background**


The 17th century saw the beginning of the decline in some of the more outlandish theories of disease. The triumph of the mechanical philosophy meant the decline of the animistic conception of the universe which constitutes the basic rationale for magical therapy. Folk medicine continued to flourish as a mixture of magic, common sense and a crude empiricism. Numerous manuals described these remedies. Samuel Thomson (1769-1843), for example, built up a system of botanicals (cf. Whorton, 1987), that his disciples were to develop into physio-medicalism (cf. Haller, 1993). In science, physio-medicalism abandoned chemical or materialistic theories of life and substituted a physiology based on vitalism. Thomsonianism never accommodated itself to orthodoxy: hence its disappearance over 60 years ago. Another systematiser was John Brown (1735-88) who posited that disease was due to excess (sthenic) or, more often, defect of stimulation (asthenic). The treatment consisted of heroic doses of stimulating drugs, often with obvious fatal results. A more successful systematiser was a contemporary of Brown and Thomson, Samuel Hahnemann (1755-1843). He embraced the vitalism of the one while moving to the opposite extreme in dosage of the other. Hahnemann revived the mediaeval doctrine of signatures in a new guise: *similia similibus* or 'like cures like'. He propounded a second law concerning the value of extremely small or infinitesimal doses. His third postulate was the doctrine of 'psora': all 'natural' chronic disorders except venereal diseases were manifestations of the psora - or itch. Homoeopathy survived because of the intellectual accommodations that homoeopathic physicians were able to make to Hahnemann's doctrines - and because of the failure of conventional physicians to demonstrate superior outcomes in the first half of the 19th century (Gevitz, 1987). Osteopathy has a similar origin. Andrew Still (1828-

1887) initially set up as a Magnetic Healer, following the doctrines of Franz Mesmer. He later combined magnetic healing and bonesetting into one doctrine: practically all diseases were due to displacements and to heal one needed to readjust the displaced segment. From the beginning, osteopaths used great freedom in selecting therapies. Today, the practice of osteopathy is largely grounded in the orthodox medical sciences and regulation removes it from the fringe to a position that is possibly both established and unorthodox (Standen, 1993). It is too easy to caricature many alternative systems by quoting the founding figure: hardly more valid than judging mainstream medicine by quoting its mistaken prophets. Neverthess, it is useful to note the twin roots of much alternative medicine in folk traditions (herbalism etc.) and/or a dominating founding figure (homoeopathy etc.). A well regulated yet unconventional practice such as modern osteopathy should not be classed with the quack, so graphically described by Young (1993). We may need to ask: is (for example) osteopathy the doctrine that Still described, what osteopaths do, or what osteopaths believe?

Keith Thomas (1971) emphasises the long link between religion and the treatment of disease. The break up of the mediaeval church aided an increasing variety in medical practice. Thus Stahl's animism takes its roots from Halle pietism (cf. Pickstone, 1982). The doctrines of Thomson and Hahnemann owed much of their success to links with dissent of all kinds: antiunionism, antiestablishment, free trade, nonconformity. In the mid 19th century, orthodoxy still offered little. Even today faith healing, which may offer at least a powerful placebo to large numbers, may be more successful in a primitive society than modern medicine which may benefit a select few (Ranger, 1982). By the late 19th century, medical education in Britain was university linked and the universities espoused naturalism in science. The decline of dissent assisted the establishment of orthodox medicine. Pluralism in medical practice was produced by patronage and the need to please the patient (Pickstone, 1982). The state backing for orthodoxy through the Medical Act of 1858 and its increasing success marginalised many alternative medical activities. It is no coincidence that a more sceptical age that questions authority and champions a consumerist faith is also an age in which complementary therapies thrive.

## Current trends

The current use of non-conventional therapies has been reviewed in the BMA report of 1993 (British Medical Association, 1993). Figures are imprecise but indicate a growing number of people using alternative therapies: 4 to 15 million consultations per year in the UK with 2,000 doctors practising such therapies. A recent survey of a panel of hospital doctors and general practitioners (BMA News Review, 1995) found that 65% of hospital doctors and 75% of GPs believed that 'complementary therapies have a place in mainstream medicine'; 35% and 45% respectively believed they 'should be widely available on the NHS'; and 75% and 73% believed doctors 'should be encouraged to learn more about complementary techniques'. Meanwhile books pour off the printing presses. Other European countries reflect these general trends. In the USA, expenditure runs into billions of dollars and evokes powerful responses:

> The frightened and vulnerable are the most common targets. Promoters traditionally appeal to the hopelessness of patients faced with what they believe is an incurable disease, play on the fear of side effects of proven treatments, provide halleluja testimonials, denigrate the physician as behind the times, and focus on the common belief that natural products have no toxicities or side effects. (Monaco and Green, 1993, p.88)

Against this background, both orthodox and non-conventional authorities acknowledge the need for regulation. All responsible practitioners have an obligation to protect the patient from fraud, even if there is disagreement about how to define it.

I will discuss common themes articulated by holistic medicine associations.


## Empiricism

The first claim of any medical treatment is that it works. Yet the history of medicine - orthodox or unconventional - is littered with thousands of treatments once enthusiastically advocated for their benefits only to be discarded. The pattern is recurrent. A new therapy is introduced by a hopeful enthusiast. Early studies or anecdotal reports suggest efficacy in most patients. These initial studies fail to control for the investigators' expectations of success. Later more adequately controlled studies appear that show the new therapy no better than inert, control, placebo therapy. The number of sceptical reports increases or another new theory appears. At this point, the treatment is abandoned and soon disappears (Benson and McCallie, 1979).

Modern medicine is the application of science to solve practical problems: those of disease or health. Advocates of complementary medicine often claim the status of a science:

> ... aromatherapy can be practised on a clinical or down-to-earth scientific level. Dr Kurt Schnaubelt's article on Oils for Viral Diseases, for instance, gives evidence of the scientific basis of clinical aromatherapy. (Wildwood,

1991, p.1)

Reflex Zone Therapy of the Feet established for itself a wholly scientific place amongst those of us studying holistic medicine. (Marquardt, 1993)

Osteopathy is the science of human mechanics. (General Council and Register of Osteopaths, 1989, p.1)

*The Science and Practice of Iridology* (Jensen, 1952)

Homoeopathy is a true science, based on the Law of Similars. (Coulter, 1985, p.57)

They should claim such status. The vital force of homoeopathy (Garion-Hutchings and Garion-Hutchings, 1991) or the 'chi' of acupuncture or the subluxed joints of chiropractic are statements about phenomena, not about abstract metaphysics or morals or aesthetics. Homoeopathy or acupuncture or chiropractic could still work without their mechanisms being understood if such entities do not exist - just as, for example, electroconvulsive therapy works in orthodoxy. But these statements too (i.e. that x works) are also empirical statements about observable phenomena - the bread and butter of science. It is surely a scandal that after nearly 200 years it is still not generally agreed that a whole system, such as homoeopathy, is anything other than placebo.

Some writers assert the existence of different sorts of science. The notion of cause and effect pervades science. Whatever the philosophical difficulties with this notion, it is impossible to conceive science, or indeed daily life, without it. But we are told that other theories of causality exist with explanatory power: Jung's synchronistic principle and in Chinese thinking. Much of this merely sounds good:

> Things behave in particular ways, not necessarily because of prior actions or impulsions of other things but because their position in the ever moving cyclical universe was such that they were endowed with intrinsic natures which made their behaviour inevitable for them. The idea of correspondence has greater significance and replaces the idea of causality for things are connected and not caused. (Pietroni, 1990, p.44).

Or again, the 'Particular Humanist's view of scientific knowledge is that it is personal, partisan, non-rational, and political' (Pietroni, 1990, p.51). This knowledge, we are told (Pietroni, 1990, p.52), comes in novels and poems: 'often far more long-lasting than those (truths) identified through a double-blind trial'. Metaphysical beliefs, poetical analogies, vivid metaphors may be more memorable than the trial of yet another beta-blocker, but this does not make them science. Science may be personal (Polanyi, 1958) but it is not partisan, for a scientific belief is held responsibly with universal intent:

> Inasmuch as scientific method lays firm emphasis on observation, measurement and reproducibility it has inevitably separated itself from doctrines embracing superstition, magic and the supernatural. It is important to realise that this separation was (and is) quite independent of therapeutic effectiveness. It seemingly represents a different conception of why observable phenomena have the effects they do. An all embracing and internally consistent theory of medical science was the result, with direct and logical consequence for success in therapeutics. (Board of Science Working Party on Alternative Therapy, 1986, p.61)

Are then these practices 'a different science' by a 'new paradigm'? Paradigm is a contentious concept, proposed by Thomas Kuhn as an important component of how science works (Kuhn, 1962). A paradigm is made up of the general theoretical assumptions and laws and techniques for their application that members of a particular scientific community adopt. Workers within a paradigm practise what Kuhn calls normal science. A mature science is governed by a single paradigm. The paradigm sets the standards for legitimate work within the science it governs. It is past work that serves as a model for future interpretations. In medicine, Stahl's animistic theory is a paradigm according to whose rules were later to emerge the phlogiston theory as well as countless vitalist doctrines and treatments in biology and medicine. A paradigm contains fairly strict rules for what counts as a scientific problem. Over time anomalous cases are collected that should conform to the paradigm but don't. Some scientist then loses faith in the paradigm and new theories are proposed. The paradigm may exist alongside another for a while but it is eventually replaced (cf. Loose, 1980, pp.203 et seq.). Advocates of competing paradigms may not understand each other because they may not fully share standards of explanation or procedures for interpreting data or beliefs about how the world works. In this way, unconventional practitioners or holists claim their work cannot be understood by orthodox medicine. Competition between paradigms cannot be resolved by proofs and is more akin to a 'conversion'. Positivism cannot therefore explain why a new paradigm is accepted. While complementary therapists would support this view, their claim for a paradigm shift cannot be accepted. Orthodox medicine proceeds according to a paradigm of modern science, whereas complementary medicine looks to a different paradigm. But what is this new paradigm? The claim that the work of complementary practitioners cannot be understood by orthodox medicine is only plausible if it has paradigmatic work, a recognised set of problems and shared (complementary or holistic) standards for what constitutes a solution to those problems. It has none of these features.

Chiropractors, iridologists, reflexologists, tongue diagnosers and zone therapists all claim to treat or diagnose the whole from some anatomical part. They differ about which part and hence about the problem.

No scientist practises in isolation, but occupies a position within a framework of institutions. A physicist, a mathematician or a doctor belongs to a particular group, a professional body. Together these groups form the scientific community. Science is not the use of a 'scientific method' so much as a discipline imposed by the community of scientists on itself in the interests of discovering truth. Only this discipline can prevent the adulteration of science by cranks and dabblers (Polanyi, 1962, p.67). The methods of scientific enquiry cannot be formulated; the authority of science is essentially traditional. 'Scientific knowledge, like language, is intrinsically the common property of a group or else nothing at all' (Kuhn, 1962, p.94). 'There is no standard higher than the assent of the relevant community' (Kuhn, 1962, p.210). Polanyi writes:

> Take two scientists discussing a problem of science on an equal footing. Each will rely on standards which he believes to be obligatory both for himself and the other. Every time either of them makes an assertion as to what is true and valuable in science, he relies blindly on a whole system of collateral facts and values accepted by science. And he relies also on it that his partner relies on the same system. Indeed, the bond of mutual trust thus formed between the two is but one link in the vast network of confidence between thousands of scientists of different specialities. Though each may dissent from some of the accepted standards of science, such heterodoxies must remain fragmentary if science is to survive as a coherent system of superior knowledge, upheld by people mutually recognising each other as scientists, and acknowledged by modern society as its guide. (Polanyi, 1958, p.375)

Now it is true that many treatments used in orthodox medicine have not been proven. Subjects recruited into clinical trials are often very different from the larger number of patients for whom a new drug may be recommended; and some practices have not been assessed in any formal way. But all form part of an articulate system of thought, all are subject to criticism as to their place in that system, all could in principle be tested and falsified; and all practices that represent extrapolations from the evidence (e.g. using a drug in the old when the trial subjects were younger) may be debated as to the reasonableness of the extrapolation. Criticism is essential to science and science pursues ever more enlightened aspirations, according to premises accepted by the scientific community. Complementary practices, by contrast, avoid critical assessment, often by insisting that every individual is different. Thus chiropractic and homoeopathy both assert individualistic significance to symptoms; psychic healers deny that healing works only through suggestion, but acknowledge that a receptive patient makes success optimal (Benor, 1985), a far from recent observation (cf. *Mark* 6, 5-6). Without generalisations, critical assessment becomes impossible. Like hypnotism, once rejected for its lack of plausibility (Polanyi, 1951, p.13; Eysenck, 1957, pp.25 et seq.), we cannot exclude the possibility of truth in all complementary therapies. But scientific opinion must do so now, both on grounds of paucity of evidence in favour of them and because of their implausibility in the current scientific conception of things.

Unfortunately, unconventional practitioners have no agreed method by which to test their truth claims. Their associations are sectarian special interest groups, not part of a wider scientific community. One must again caution: much has changed in the last 10 years, but it remains broadly true for most of the 116 therapies and practices listed in the BMA report (Board of Science Working Party on Alternative Therapy, 1986). There is a growing amount of serious work. But compared to orthodoxy, there is little critical exchange among practitioners. Most publications do not meet reputable scientific standards and the number of studies in peer reviewed general medical journals is tiny. The recent BMA (British Medical Association, 1993) survey is revealing. Of 40 organisations approached, 27 responded. Only 12 claimed publications in peer-reviewed journals and of these 3 were 'in-house' journals of the specialty. 14 organisations published a journal, 5 a newsletter and 8 nothing. Most appeared to have little involvement with research. Holistic or complementary medicine is not a scientific tradition; its advocates are cranks, not scientists. It is not bad science, but pseudo-science.

Advocates of unconventional therapies are understandably reluctant to advise how to identify an effective system of treatment. Any success is adduced as evidence in favour of the treatment, no matter under what conditions (Radner and Radner, 1985). There is a heavy reliance on personal testimonials. Or we are told that 'a million people can't be wrong'. But it is a mark of pseudo-science to believe quantity of evidence makes up for its quality. Confirmation of an hypothesis will increase with the number of favourable test findings (Hempel, 1966) but the increase becomes smaller with each successive test. If the new finding is from a different test, however, the confirmation will be significantly enhanced. Diverse evidence strengthens a conclusion in science, provided such diversity is relevant. If we believe propranolol works as a drug by beta-blocking actions, its effect on slowing the exercising heart confirms our hypothesis, but with each successive subject the additional evidence adds less. If we diversify by doing different exercises or doing them at night, it adds nothing. But if we measure another beta-adrenergic effect, say airways resistance, and find it alters this, the hypothesis is significantly strengthened. If we make a new observation, not previously considered and find this confirms, the evidence is even stronger. Logically, of course, the strength of support depends on what the hypothesis asserts and what the data are. Whether the hypothesis or its test implication came first is historical and should not count. Nevertheless, an hypothesis is strengthened 'from above' if deduction from an already existing theory adds to its inductive-evidential support, i.e. our hypothesis forms part of an articulate system of thought. Thus if it is believed that the sympathetic nervous system mediates the consequences of an acute anxiety state, we may deduce that beta-blockade will be an effective symptomatic treatment. The discovery that propranolol is effective in this way therefore fits a wider, more embracing theory of the role of catecholamines in neurological function. Diversity of evidence and theoretical support by deduction from accepted scientific laws is almost always lacking for alternative therapies: hence the demand for a 'new paradigm'.

Arguments from spurious similarity are another mark of pseudo-science (Radner and Radner, 1985). For example, homoeopathy posits an energy field or 'vital force'. Disease is a disorder of the body's energy field. The energy field of the medicine stimulates the body's own fluid to induce healing. The principle cited is the interchangeability of energy and matter. Now scientists do defend new proposals on the grounds of compatibility with current knowledge. They will also draw analogies from one field to illuminate work in another. For example, one may draw analogies about the way neuro-transmitters work at the neuromuscular junction with the way certain hormones attach to their receptors. But a new proposal is not true *because* it is compatible with previous work, nor is it true *because* an analogy can be drawn. For example, an analogy has been drawn between homoeopathy and Einstein's Relativity theory. Einstein demonstrated interchangeability of matter and energy. By analogy, it has been suggested that when homoeopathic medicines have been so diluted that no active molecules remain, energy has been transferred to the liquid. This argument from spurious similarity to Einstein is false. The energy in the molecules of the medicinal substance leaves the solution when the molecules leave. The analogy between homoeopathy and Einstein's Relativity Theory is false.

## Personal responsibility

If the assertion of personal responsibility in health implied the advocacy of more healthy life styles, almost everyone would agree. A more substantive claim is often made by holistic practitioners: that individuals *are* responsible for their health. Now sometimes we are responsible for our health in that our actions have unhealthy consequences. If we smoke we may develop bronchitis or lung cancer. Responsibility then means acting in a different way - stopping smoking for example. Such a concept of responsibility is uncontroversial, although what responsibility means in practice may be.

The holist emphasis on responsibility extends further. Many believe that patients can influence events by adopting treatments for illnesses whose causes are always multifactorial and often not fully known. They are therefore more likely to endorse the suggestion that 'unhealthy' actions are causally responsible for the illness. This is a difference that stems from empirical beliefs, not in the concept of responsibility. Holists go further in developing 'positive autonomy'. This refers to active, purposive, effective direction of one's personal affairs that is not only efficacious in preventing or curing illness, but good in itself. In this respect, holists recommend a life style, not merely a particular treatment mode. We may contrast this with 'negative autonomy', i.e. the absence of constraints on freedom. Positive autonomy is valued for more than its effect on health as ordinarily conceived. Many holistic writers endorse positive autonomy. One is urged to 'go for positive happiness', 'to stop, examine, and choose' (Ardell, 1977, p.110). Self responsibility for holistic nurses means 'the reflective response of the self to freely choose from a variety of alternatives' (Blattner, 1981, p.34). In the holistic vocabulary, personal reponsibility in this sense *is* health. Holism, philosophically, then becomes a theory of the good. This view of responsibility raises two problems: liability and duty.

The commonest sense of responsibility has more to do with liability (hence blame, praise etc.) than with cause or positive autonomy. To judge someone responsible is to render him or her liable to sanctions (or deserving approbation) and to exculpate or at least mitigate the responsibility of others. In the context of holism personal reponsibility for health leads to blaming the victim whilst exonerating the factors, known or unknown, that made him sick, and excusing the medical intervention that failed to restore health. Holists are in fact divided by this implication of responsibility (Wikler, 1985). For some the acceptance of illness as beyond one's control may serve the holistic aim of inner peace; for others reponsibility is an example of anachronistic thinking in which disease is punishment for moral failure.

Another sense of responsibility is that of duty. If it is my duty to be somewhere, I am responsible for being there. To whom then might one be responsible or have a duty for health? One answer might be the state. Illness loses productivity by which all benefit and all lose by the cost of my care. Health as public duty might justify taxes on alcohol or smoking, seat belts, selective immunisation and so on. The holistic emphasis on individualism could suggest the notion of duties to oneself. Duties however can usually be waived by the party to whom a duty is owed: if one felt like it one could erase a duty to oneself. The essence of duty, however, is an obligation even in the absence of inclination. We may go further. A healthy lifestyle may not be considered worthwhile. The rewards of a job may be worth its risks, the pleasures of a sport worth its dangers, the avoidance of conscription worth an actual illness. The notion of a duty to the self that leaves the self worse off is incoherent.

Personal responsibility for health is ambiguous. The holistic emphasis is either acceptably banal (though important) or rhetorical with no distinctive content.

## Concepts of health

Holists want to define health positively, not (merely) as absence of disease. Many therefore re-echo the WHO definition of health as 'a state of complete physical, mental and social well-being and not merely the absence of disease or infirmity'. This global view of health focuses concern on social and psychological factors in disease, many of which are well documented. Health in these terms seems an inspiring aspiration. Two objections may be made.

Firstly, if health is a state of well-being it is is impossible to be healthy and not be in a state of well-being. Yet if health contributes to well-being, it is surely only part of it. Other things also contribute: friendship, pleasure, social life and so on. This may not trouble those who elevate holism to a philosophy of good. If happiness is healthy and dissatisfaction, anger etc., unhealthy, the holist notion of personal responsibility subsumes health under a hedonistic morality.

Secondly, the identification of health and well-being produces an unrealistic view of the obligations of health workers. It makes sense for a doctor to eradicate disease in a patient. An obligation to enquire about gardening or tiddlywinks, or to prescribe Mozart or knitting, is hardly the task of health workers (Kopelman and Moskop, 1981). It would be impossible to agree the goals or the means, still less to make the right provision. Certain goals are surely illegitimate. Happiness cannot be the aim of the psychiatrist's endeavours, nor can the average GP realistically aim to abolish the frequent complaint of being 'tired all the time'.

Sacks has pointed out that well-being may occasionally be the result of disease. Paradoxically we may then construe health as a state of disease. A radical interpretation: even the W.H.O. definition assumes the absence of disease as a necessary, though not sufficient condition of health. The paradox of illness which can present as wellness is one of the chimaeras, tricks and ironies of nature (Sacks, 1985, p.83). Hypomania is the most obvious example, but Sacks also instances others including his own descriptions of levodopa treated post-encephalitic Parkinsonism (Sacks, 1982). Such enhanced wellness always leads to extravagance, to eventual disintegration and un-control. It is well-being that leads to suffering as surely as the alcoholic's first drink. Enhanced wellness may be desired. Dostoievski writes:

> You all, healthy people, can't imagine the happiness which we epileptics feel during the second before our fit. ... I don't know if this felicity lasts for seconds, hours or months, but believe me, I would not exchange it for all the joys that life may bring.

and

> During these five seconds I live a whole human existence and for that I would give my whole life and not think that I was paying too dearly. (Dostoievski, 1931, part III, chapter 5, section 5)

Health defined as well-being would imply such experiences as legitimate goals for health workers to promote. The holist equation of health with well-being ignores the existence both of health without well-being and the existence of well-being with desired disease. It makes little sense of the observation that our subjective feeling of healthiness has decreased even though there have been major advances in our actual, objective health status (Barsky, 1988).


**Reductionism and the whole person**

Most complementary therapists claim to treat the 'whole person' even though the modality of treatment may only affect one part of the body - as in iridology, reflexology or chiropractic. This is often accompanied by references to Cartesian dualism (Pietroni, 1987; Pelletier, 1979). References to Descartes' writings or analysis of what he wrote are never given. The impression is that Descartes postulated an unbridgable gap between body and mind. He did not.

Holism is a term first coined in 1926 by J.C. Smuts and gave rise to dispute in the philosophy of biology. Smuts explicitly opposed vitalism, understood as an immaterial 'vital force' or 'vital principle' possessed by living beings: 'A living organism is not an organism plus life, as if life were something different and additional to it' (Smuts, 1926, p.110).

Nevertheless even Smuts did not clearly define holism and by the fifth chapter of his book there are already nine defining statements (Poynton, 1987). Imprecision and distortion in its use have occurred since. Smuts was also opposing a view of mechanism in biology. Whereas holists frequently oppose mechanism by recourse to vitalism, Smuts stressed that the whole was more than the sum of its parts, but not (*contra* vitalism) something added to its parts. Smuts' project was to explain how evolution can be creative, i.e.

how higher levels of wholes (e.g. life) emerge from lower levels (e.g. matter) (Brandon, 1985). Darwinian natural selection tells us only why the unfit failed to survive and not why living beings, either fit or unfit, ever came into existence (Polanyi, 1958, p.35). Smuts and J.S. Haldane argued that parts changed when synthesised into a whole to function differently. In medicine, extreme holists would seem to suggest that no analysis of the whole person in terms of his parts will yield knowledge about the whole. This implies that description of the behaviour of the whole is possible, but a complete analysis of this behaviour is not possible and therefore should not be attempted. The success of mechanistic science is reason enough to reject this view, even if mechanistic explanations cannot fully specify wholes. Learning to assemble an engine doesn't tell us what a car is for, but does tell us something about it.

A more moderate holist view might not suggest the need to eliminate mechanistic analysis, but that organised wholes occur at various levels, so mechanistic explanations must be given at that level. This demonstrates that mechanism and reductionism are different concepts, although almost always confused in holistic medicine.

We might modify this to a moderate holist view that acknowledges the value of reductionism without accepting that such explanations can ever be complete. Things may exist in hierarchies or on different levels, but the laws governing a lower level may still possess valuable explanatory power. As Bunge (1977) puts it, we may combine ontological pluralism (i.e. the recognition of variety) with epistemological reductionism (i.e. that higher levels can be partly explained in terms of lower ones). The holist protest against radical reductionism is surely necessary, though hardly a distinctive feature of the alternative medicine lobby. The claim of radical reductionism that all of the concepts, hypotheses and theories concerning things at a given level can in principle be reduced to those referring to things belonging to some other level may have been productive especially in physics from 1600 to 1800 but even here it is no longer credible. Quantum electrodynamics, quantum mechanics and the relativistic theory of gravitation are not reducible to one another, if only because they deal with things of radically different kinds. Still less is this possible in biology, where phenomena emerge with properties at one level of organisation that are not present at other levels of organisation. Biological systems have no vital force or principle but do have properties not predicted or predictable from chemical laws or theory. Life is not a chemical property, but the statistical regularities of biological systems involve chemicals doing things not predicted by chemical laws. Biochemistry sets the boundary conditions: biological laws are additional. Perception, imagination, emotion, memory and so on are not predicted by the simple function of nervous cells. Psychological function may be independent of

117

neurological correlates and the laws of memory and perception can be worked out without recourse to neural laws. The capacity for abstraction and symbolism takes man beyond the world of immediate experience in a quest for meaning. This is meta-biological emergence. Emergence is not an obscure notion and does not have to be either accepted on faith (holism) or rejected with contempt (radical reductionism).

Generally speaking holists pay little attention to the large literature on reductionism in biology so the concept is used loosely. Hull (1981) for example, discriminates between ontological, methodological and theory reduction. The first asserts that organisms are 'nothing but' atoms, to which anti-reductionists contrast structured (i.e. ordered) wholes. Methodological reduction concerns optimal strategies in science; while theory reduction seeks to explain one theory in terms of another. For example, classical Mendelian genetics may be explained in terms of molecular biology. Such explanations are fruitful in the research programmes that surround scientific theories. Thus Tay-Sachs disease at the level of the whole patient is shown to be due to an enzyme deficiency at the biochemical level; which in turn may be shown to be due to an abnormal gene at the genetic or molecular biological level. Hence rationally based genetic counselling emerges (Zucker, 1981; Schaffner, 1981). Reductive explanations in medicine are marked by appeals to genetic, biochemical and physicochemical causes of disease features. They need not be strictly deductive, i.e. their content distinguishes them, not their logical form. For example, we may say that smoking causes lung cancer. There is a large body of evidence to support this, but the epidemiological evidence does not permit a strictly deductive conclusion about the behaviour of the bronchial mucosal cell from the behaviour of populations. The content of this argument gives it explanatory power. Reductionism has led to much progress and it is only a prejudice to believe this incompatible with caring medicine.

Holists insist on the multifactorial nature of disease, but reductionism does not deny this. Von Pettenkofer drank a vial of cholera bacilli and did not suffer. He therefore demonstrated that other factors besides bacterial ingestion were important. There is no logical or empirical reason to believe that reductionistic medicine will fail to seek and find an actual multifactorial mechanism. What holists are usually about however is an emphasis on psychosomatic mechanisms and the distinctiveness of every patient. But psychological states do not have to be strictly identical for generalisations to be made any more than all apples have to be the same size in order to generalise about apples. The more extreme claim that all disease is psychosomatic is even less defensible, for there is no sense in which rubella or motor neurone disease or a host of others are caused psychosomatically. Orthodox medicine has never denied causal relationships between mind and body: anger causes the face to flush, fever causes delirium. There is no reason why a psychological event could not cause a physical event if every psychological event is associated with a physical event. The mind/brain interaction may be poorly understood, but that is no reason to postulate spiritual forces - or to retreat to a dualistic view of mind and body that holism simultaneously claims to avoid (Clark, 1985). Once again holism dresses up a simple but important truism - consider psychological factors in the cause and response to disease - as a distinctive contribution to medicine.


## Natural, mystic and antique

'You could have the best of both worlds - better health naturally - by using the experience and wisdom from ancient cultures and combining modern science.' So ran the leaflet advertising a herbal remedy I was given. Some complementary therapies place great emphasis on natural means, on their antique roots and on cultural origins - often linked to Eastern mysticism.

Modern medicine has been rightly criticised for iatrogenesis: the result of an overweening pharmaceutical industry pushing chemical cures to maximise profits. Indeed, the chief role of physicians is sometimes portrayed as purveyors of drugs (General Council and Register of Osteopaths, 1989, p.2). Against this caricature, the 'natural' is emphasised for its overtones of purity, gentleness and, above all, its lack of side-effects. Now it is true that many unconventional approaches do indeed lack direct side-effects, not least because they have no direct effects of any sort. But other approaches are far from problem free (Board of Science Working Party on Alternative Therapy, 1986; Bender, 1985, esp. pp.66-74; Gill et al., 1994). The National Poisons Unit at St Thomas' Hospital investigated 5,563 emergency case enquiries: symptoms of poisoning suspected to be related to traditional remedies and food supplements were reported in 657 (12%) of these (St Thomas' Hospital Gazette, 1995). Herbs can kill (Vautier and Spiller, 1995); acupuncture can cause serious disease (Jeffreys et al., 1983). A natural substance is no more hazard free in principle than a synthetic one. The claims made are often simply untrue:

A synthetic chemical is, in theory, identical to that found in nature; in practice, as every chemist knows, it is impossible to make a 100% pure chemical. Any synthetic chemical will carry with it a small percentage of undesirable substances which are not found in the essential oil. ... a synthetic chemical lacks the life force found only in nature. (Wildwood, 1991, p.9)

Needless to say, such statements are made with no supporting evidence - quite apart from the explicit vitalism. The biggest side effect from unconventional

119

therapy may be the harm that results from delayed appropriate treatment - a well publicised example of which led to a conviction for manslaughter for the parents of a diabetic child in 1994 (Myers, 1993).

The emphasis on traditional and ancient roots is yet another image building aspect of unconventional therapies: ancient China for herbal medicine and acupuncture, ancient Egypt for aromatherapy, ancient India and North American Indians for reflexology and so on. The emphasis on continuity is reassuring for many, but it carries no connection with efficacy. It is not difficult to think of traditional practices that are thoroughly harmful, however 'natural' the products employed.

The appeal to Eastern mysticism is a third feature that evokes sympathy in the undiscerning, perhaps especially to a generation that has rejected so much of its own religious traditions and looks to a numinous East. Modern scientific medicine is largely a creation of the Western world; however appealing Eastern 'philosophy' - and the word philosophy means more of a world outlook than the logical discipline that the word encompasses in British universities - it has no association with the power to heal disease. Of course, it may be valuable for many people: it may bring serenity in distress, strengthen resolution or give meaning to life. The geneticist, Galton, demonstrated the lack of association between amplitude and frequency of prayer and longevity in a paper that was far from crudely irreligious (Medawar, 1968, p.76). Eastern philosophy - whatever that is - is likely to be no different in that respect. It is usually poorly defined in accounts of unconventional therapies.

### Does it all matter?

Some time ago, a mother of two young children arrived in hospital under my care after taking a large overdose of drugs. She had carcinoma of the breast with secondary spread and had been treated at an alternative centre. She had been recommended a bizarre diet and counselled to search for the cause of the cancer within her. It was all too much and she decided to end it all. I don't doubt that her advisers were dedicated and well intentioned and idealistic and as honourable as Brutus. But the result was dreadful. Of course, popular magazines are full of orthodox medical disasters, but part of holism's appeal is its claim to avoid such situations. We should protest against inappropriate use of technology of all sorts, but it too easily becomes a protest against technology itself (Jennett, 1986, p.275). We should be against impersonal medicine, but not against technical competence; against medical arrogance but not against medical expertise; against self-serving guildism but not against professional ideals; against obscurantism but not against science. Compare

Illich's description of that popular Aunt Sally, the intensive care unit, with Medawar's view: 'Intensive care is but the culmination of a public worship organised around a medical priesthood struggling against death' (Illich, 1976, p.114); 'It was as allies, then, that I regarded my physicians and the apparatus of intensive care and not as so many plots to deprive me of my dignity' (Medawar, 1983, p.277).

Modern medicine with its military metaphors (the 'fight' against cancer, the 'battle' against microbes, aggressive therapy etc.) may have promised more than it can deliver: still disappointingly little for many degenerative and malignant diseases. But its achievements have been spectacular and progress continues. It is well designed scientific studies that provide the evidence upon which unsound orthodox practices can be revised or abandoned, not appeals to magic or irrationalism. The vitalism that pervades so many complementary medical theories represents mediaeval animism writ small. It is a return to an all embracing theory that saves the intellectual task of comprehending the complexities of modern science. It is not surprising that expertise in many complementary therapies can be acquired without lengthy, rigorous training (Wolpert, 1987). John Webster remarked in 1677:

> there is no greater folly than to be very inquisitive and laborious to find out the causes of such a phenomenon as never had any existence, and therefore men ought to be cautious and to be fully assured of the truth of the effect before they adventure to explicate the cause. (Webster, 1677, p.251)

The laetrile saga (Relman, 1982) should have taught us that medical science cannot afford to waste its resources disproving every crazy idea. Encouraging the scientifically unsound is the practice of deceit, the abandonment of commitment to the truth, a surrender to irrationalism and magic.


## Bibliography

Ardell, D.B. (1977), *High Level Wellness*, Rodale, Emmaus, Pa.

Barsky, A.J. (1988), 'The paradox of health', *New England Journal of Medicine*, 318, pp.414-18.

Bayliss, R.I.S. (1988), 'The National Health Service versus private and complementary medicine', *British Medical Journal*, 296, pp.1457-59.

Bender, A.E. (1985), *Health Or Hoax?* Sphere Books, London.

Benor, D.J. (1985), 'Psychic healing', in Salmon, J.W. (ed.), *Alternative Medicines, Popular and Policy Perspectives*, Tavistock Publications, London, pp.165-190.

Benson, H. and McCallie, D.P. (1979), 'Angina pectoris and the placebo effect', *New England Journal of Medicine*, 300, pp.1424-28.

Blattner, B. (1981), *Holistic Nursing*, Prentice-Hall, Englewood Cliffs, N.J.

Board of Science Working Party on Alternative Therapy (1986), *Alternative Therapies. Report of the Board of Science Working Party on Alternative Therapy*, British Medical Association, London.

Brandon, R.N. (1985), 'Holism in the philosophy of biology', in Glymour, C. and Stalker, D. (eds), *Examining Holistic Medicine*, Prometheus Books, Buffalo, New York, pp.127-146.

British Medical Association (1993), *Complementary Medicine: New Approaches to Good Practice*, Oxford University Press, Oxford.

*BMA News Review*, July 1995.

Bunge, M. (1977), 'Levels and reduction', *American Journal of Physiology*, 233, R75-R82.

Bynum, W.F. and Porter, R. (1987), *Medical Fringe and Medical Orthodoxy 1750-1850*, Croom Helm, London.

Clark, A. (1985), 'Psychological causation and the concept of psychosomatic disease', in Glymour, C. and Stalker, D. (eds), *Examining Holistic Medicine*, Prometheus Books, Buffalo, New York, pp.67-106.

Coulter, H.L. (1985), 'Homoeopathy' in Salmon, J.W. (ed.), *Alternative Medicines, Popular and Policy Perspectives*, Tavistock Publications, London, pp.57-9.

Dostoievski, F. (1931), *The Possessed*, (trans. C. Garnett) Everyman's Library, Dent, London.

Eysenck, H.J. (1957), *Sense and Nonsense in Psychology*, Penguin, Harmondsworth, Middlesex.

Garion-Hutchings, N. and Garion-Hutchings, S. (1991), *The Concise Guide to Homoeopathy*, Element Books, Shaftesbury, Dorset.

General Council and Register of Osteopathy (1989), *Osteopathy: Your Questions Answered*, General Council and Register of Osteopathy, London.

Gevitz, N. (1987), 'Sectarian medicine', *Journal of the American Medical Association*, 257, pp.1636-40.

Gill, G.V., Redmond, S., Garratt, F., and Paisey, R. (1994), 'Diabetes and alternative medicine: cause for concern', *Diabetic Medicine*, 11, pp.210-13.

Glymour, C. and Stalker, G. (1985), 'Why examine holistic medicine?', in Glymour, C. and Stalker, G. (eds), *Examining Holistic Medicine*, Prometheus Books, Buffalo, New York, pp.9-17.

Haller, J. (1993), 'Kindly medicines. A history of physio-medicals in American Medicine', *New York State Journal of Medicine*, 93, pp.133-141.

Hempel, C.G. (1966), *Philosophy of Natural Science*, Prentice Hall, New York.

Henney, J.E. (1993), 'Combatting medical fraud', *New York State Journal of Medicine*, 93, pp.86-7.

Hull, D.L. (1981), 'Reduction and genetics', *Journal of Medicine and Philosophy*, 6, pp.93-100.

Illich, I. (1976), *Limits To Medicine*, Penguin, Harmondsworth, Middlesex.

Inglis, Brian. (1964), *Fringe Medicine*, Faber and Faber, London.

Jeffreys, D.B., Smith, S., Roper, B., and Curry, P.V.L. (1983), 'Acupuncture needles as a cause of bacterial endocarditis', *British Medical Journal*, 287, pp.326-7.

Jennett, B. (1986), *High Technology Medicine. Benefits and Burdens*, Oxford University Press, Oxford.

Jensen, B. (1952), *The Science and Practice of Iridology*, Jensen, Escondido, California.

Kopelman, L. and Moskop, J. (1981), 'The holistic health movement: a survey and a critique', *Journal of Medicine and Philosophy*, 6, pp.209-235.

Kuhn, T. (1962), *The Structure of Scientific Revolutions*, University of Chicago Press, Chicago.

Lewith, G. (1993), 'Complementary medicine: new approaches to good practice. An appraisal of the BMA report', *Complementary Therapies in Medicine*, 1, pp.218-220.

Lister, J. (1983), 'Current controversy on alternative medicine', *New England Journal of Medicine*, 309, pp.1524-26.

Loose, J. (1980), *A Historical Introduction to the Philosophy of Science*, Oxford University Press, Oxford.

Marquardt, H. (1993), *Reflex Zone Therapy of the Feet*, Thorsons Publishing Group, Wellingborough, Northants.

Medawar, P. (1968), 'Induction and intuition in scientific thought', in Medawar, P. (ed.) (1985), *Pluto's Republic*, Oxford University Press, Oxford.

Medawar, P. (1983), 'The life instinct and dignity in dying', in Pyke, D. (ed.) (1991), *The Threat and the Glory*, Oxford University Press, Oxford.

Monaco, G.P. and Green, S. (1993), 'Recognising deception in the promotion of untested and uproven medical treatments', *New York State Journal of Medicine*, 93, pp.88-91.

Myers, P. (1993), 'Alternative cure 'zealot' jailed for daughter's death', *The Guardian*, 6 November.

*New York State Journal of Medicine*, Vol. 93, No. 2, 1993.

Pelletier, K.R. (1979), *Holistic Medicine: From Stress to Optimum Health*, Dell Publishing Co., New York.

Pietroni, P. (1987), 'The meaning of illness: holism dissected', *Journal of the Royal Society of Medicine*, 80, pp.357-360.

Pietroni, P. (1990), *The Greening of Medicine*, Gollancz, London.

Pietroni, P. (1992), 'Beyond the boundaries: relationships between general practice and complementary therapy', *British Medical Journal*, 305, pp.564-66.

Pickstone, J.V. (1982), 'Establishment and dissent in nineteenth century medicine: an explanation of some correspondence and connections between religious and medical belief systems in early industrial England', in Shiels, W.J. (ed.), *The Church and Healing*, Ecclesiastical History Society Series, Vol. 19, Basil Blackwell, Oxford. pp.165-190.

Polanyi, M. (1951), *The Logic of Liberty*, Routledge and Kegan Paul, London.

Polanyi, M. (1958), *Personal Knowledge*, Routledge and Kegan Paul, London.

Polanyi, M. (1962), 'The republic of science' in Grene, M. (ed.) (1969), *Knowing and Being: Essays by Michael Polanyi*, University of Chicago Press, Chicago, pp.49-72.

Poynton, J.C. (1987), 'Smuts's holism and evolution sixty years on', *Transactions of the Royal Society of South Africa*, 46, pp.181-9.

Radner, D. and Radner, M. (1985), 'Holistic methodology and pseudoscience', in and Glymour, C. and Stalker, D. (eds), *Examining Holistic Medicine*, Prometheus Books, Buffalo, New York, pp.149-159.

Ranger, T. (1982), 'Medical science and Pentecost: the dilemma of Anglicanism in Africa', in Shiels, W.J. (ed.), *The Church and Healing*, Ecclesiastical History Society Series, Vol. 19, Basil Blackwell, Oxford, pp.333-366.

Relman, A. (1982), 'Closing the book on laetrile', *New England Journal of Medicine*, 306, p.236.

Sacks, O. (1982), *Awakenings*, Picador, London.

Sacks, O. (1985), *The Man Who Mistook His Wife For A Hat*, Picador, London.

*St Thomas' Hospital Gazette*, Spring 1995.

Schaffner, K.F. (1981), 'Reduction and holism in medicine', *Journal of Medicine and Philosophy*, 6, pp.93-100.

Smith, T.(1983), 'Alternative medicine', *British Medical Journal*, 287, p.307.

Smuts, J.C. (1926), *Holism and Evolution*, Macmillan, London.

Standen, C.S. (1993), 'The implications of the Osteopaths Act', *Complementary Therapies in Medicine*, 1, pp.208-210.

Sydenham, T. (1668), *Methodus Curandi Febres*, Second edition, London.

Thomas, K. (1971), *Religion and the Decline of Magic*, Peregrine, Penguin Books, Harmondsworth, Middlesex.

Vautier, G. and Spiller, R.C. (1995), 'Safety of complementary medicine should be monitored', *British Medical Journal*, 311, p.633.

Webster, J. (1677), *The Displaying of Supposed Witchcraft*.

Whorton, J.C. (1987), 'Traditions of folk medicine in America', *Journal of the American Medical Association*, 257, pp.1632-35.

Wikler, D. (1985), 'Holistic medicine: concepts of personal responsibility for health', in Glymour, C. and Stalker, D. (eds), *Examining Holistic Medicine*, Prometheus Books, Buffalo, New York, pp.137-146.

Wildwood, C. (1991), *Aromatherapy*, Element Books, Shaftesbury, Dorset.

Wolpert, L. (1987), 'Science and anti-science. The Lloyd Roberts lecture 1986', *Journal of the Royal College of Physicians of London*, 21, pp.159-165.

Young, J.H. (1993), 'The paradise of quacks', *New York State Journal of Medicine*, 93, pp.127-133.

Zucker, A. (1981), 'Holism and reductionism: a view from genetics', *Journal of Medicine and Philosophy*, 6, pp.145-163.

# 8 Defining intellectual disability

*Steven Edwards*

This paper begins by pointing to the apparently low moral status accorded to individuals said to be intellectually disabled.[1] Given this, it is clear that the question of whether there are clear criteria for being legitimately categorised as intellectually disabled is an important one. It is suggested in part two that there appear not to be clear criteria for the determination of the presence of intellectual disability; and in part three it is claimed that, even if there were, attempts to link moral status to intelligence may be independently objectionable. Part four of the paper focuses on McCullough's (1984) criticisms of 'fixed-state' construals of intellectual disability, and upon his claim that there is a 'world-gained' to individuals described as being intellectually disabled. In conclusion, an attempt is made to outline five conditions of adequacy on definitions of intellectual disability.

## Moral status

The aim of this section is to set out the claim that the moral status accorded to individuals deemed to possess characteristics or properties associated with intellectual disability is compromised by the mere fact of the presence or likely presence of such properties. Before this can be undertaken, however, a few brief remarks concerning the notion of moral status are necessary.

It is plausible to claim that the moral status of individual things is determined by certain factors. Humans are standardly taken to have a higher moral status than inanimate objects such as tables, chairs, stones etc. Reasons for this view include the claims that humans experience sensations such as pleasure and pain, and are capable of rational thought.

More controversially, it remains widely held - though not undisputed - that humans have a higher moral status than members of other species. A frequently posited justification for this is, again, that humans, in general, have

127

the capacity to engage in rational thought. So even within the class of sentient things, a moral hierarchy is typically posited with humans at its highest point.

Indicators of moral status include the degree of justification required to act in certain ways towards individuals, and the ways in which certain actions are regarded. Thus, throwing a stone into a pond cannot be said to harm the stone; and no justification beyond the fact that one felt like doing it would normally be expected. But throwing a person into a pond may be taken to constitute a great moral wrong; and an attempt to justify the act on the grounds that one simply felt like doing it would not be considered adequate. So the degree of justification required to undertake certain types of acts is an indicator of the moral status of certain types of individuals.

Given acceptance of the claim that humans are considered to have a higher moral status than other kinds of things, it is evident that even within the class of humans, there are apparent differences in moral status. In English law the human foetus has a lower status than a healthy adult since it is lawful to actively bring about the death of a foetus, but is not lawful to actively bring about the death of a healthy adult or child. Presumably, this legal position reflects a moral consensus regarding the status of the human foetus among the citizens of the UK to the effect that it has a moral status which is lower than that enjoyed by more developed humans. So even within the class of humans, there are differences in moral status.

It can be claimed that those human individuals described variously as being mentally subnormal, mentally retarded, mentally handicapped, as individuals with learning difficulties, or intellectual disabilities are accorded a lower moral status than non-disabled individuals (cf. McCullough, 1984; Kopelman, 1984). At least four considerations can be offered to support this claim.

First, it is the case that a pregnancy may be terminated on the grounds that the foetus is likely to develop intellectual disability (e.g. as in tests for Down's Syndrome such as amniocentesis). Hence, the mere grounds that the resulting infant is thought likely to develop such a disability are apparently considered sufficient to warrant termination of the pregnancy. This is the case even if the foetus is healthy.[2]

So although the human foetus may have a lower moral status than that of an adult human or child, the moral status of a foetus which is likely to develop intellectual disability is considered lower still. This follows since the mere likelihood of such a disability is sufficient grounds for termination.

Second, until very recently, if it was determined that a neonate had a condition associated with intellectual disability (e.g. Down's Syndrome) this was considered sufficient grounds to omit to nourish the infant and thus allow it to die (Khuse and Singer, 1985, pp.3-10). Mason and McCall Smith indicate that English law remained ambiguous on this matter until 1990 (1994, p.153). Of course, it has never been considered legitimate from the moral or legal perspectives to act in this way towards non-disabled neonates.

Third, the views of personhood canvassed by Harris (1985) amongst others can be taken to lend support to the view that the moral status of individuals with severe mental disability is less than that of other humans. This is due to the relationship between moral status and rationality which is posited by such commentators. Lack of awareness of the capabilities of individuals with, say, Down's Syndrome can lead one to suppose that such individuals would fail to meet such criteria.

Fourth, the very terminology employed to refer to persons with intellectual disabilities appears to signify a degree of moral status lower than that accorded to other persons. Books and articles may be found which include references to 'the mentally subnormal' (Todd, 1967), 'the mentally retarded' (McCullough, 1984) and to 'the mentally deficient' (Clarke et al., 1985). This language evidently characterises individuals exhaustively in terms of their lack of a property which is considered highly desirable; namely intelligence or cognitive capacity. Further, in ordinary, nontechnical contexts such terms are commonly employed as terms of abuse e.g. 'retard', 'LD', and so on.

In the light of the claim that one's moral status seems affected by being legitimately described as intellectually disabled (etc.), it seems extremely important to have sound criteria for membership of that class of individuals. With this aim in mind, we can turn to consideration of the legal definition of mental impairment.

**Conceptual problems: problems of definition**

In a section entitled 'The Concept of Mental Handicap' Heaton-Ward and Wiley (1984, p.1) point out that in the 1983 Mental Health Act the terms 'mental subnormality' and 'severe mental subnormality' which figure in the 1959 Act are replaced by 'mental impairment' and 'severe mental impairment'. They suggest that the terms 'mental handicap' and 'severe mental handicap' are employed in non-legal, everyday contexts but the 1983 Act avoids this terminology. The reason, it appears, is to distinguish the majority of persons with intellectual disabilities from a small percentage of persons who are intellectually disabled but who are in need of certain special kinds of services - compulsory care for example (Heaton-Ward and Wiley, 1984, p.1).

The definition of 'mental impairment' offered in The Mental Health Act 1983 runs as follows:

Severe mental impairment - a state of arrested or incomplete development of mind, which includes severe impairment of intelligence and social functioning and is associated with abnormally aggressive or seriously irresponsible conduct on the part of the person concerned.

Mental impairment - a state of arrested or incomplete development of mind (not amounting to severe mental impairment), which includes significant impairment of intelligence and social functioning and is associated with abnormally aggressive or seriously irresponsible conduct on the part of the person concerned. (quoted in Heaton-Ward and Wiley, 1984, p.108)

The definitions of mental impairment and severe mental impairment offered in the 1983 Act are claimed to be much narrower than those of the equivalent terms in the 1959 Act. A distinction is presumed between individuals who may be described as being intellectually disabled and those covered by the provisions of the Act: i.e. those deemed mentally impaired or severely mentally impaired (see also, Clarke et al., 1985, p.34). (In what follows I ignore the distinction between severe mental impairment and mental impairment.) Evidently, those who are mentally impaired form a subset of the class of persons said to have intellectual disabilities.

In an attempt to clarify the meaning of the term 'intellectual disability' and cognate terms, I propose to consider further the terms which figure in the 1983 Act. This may prove profitable since, as noted, the individuals covered by the Act form a subset of those describable as intellectually disabled. Hence, it should be possible to identify the conditions necessary for an individual to be classified as being intellectually disabled.

*The 1983 definitions*

It is evident that the Act appeals centrally to the following six criteria: (i) arrested development of mind; (ii) incomplete development of mind; (iii) impairment of intelligence (significant or severe); (iv) impairment of social functioning; (v) abnormally aggressive behaviour; and (vi) seriously irresponsible conduct.

Each of these criteria can be considered, critically, in two ways. A first way involves an attempt to show the criteria to be ambiguous or unclear. And a second way seeks to establish which of the criteria are the defining features of mental impairment; in other words, which constitute the necessary and sufficient conditions of mental impairment. Let us now consider each of the criteria in these two ways: firstly for clarity, and secondly in terms of necessary and sufficient conditions.

(i) The expression 'arrested development of mind' seems open to challenge on grounds of unclarity. For example, it may be said of a person in a dull, routine kind of occupation that his mind has ceased to develop - that the process of development of his cognitive faculties has arrested.

But suppose that an adequate definition of 'arrested development of mind' could be given. Would such a state constitute a *necessary* condition of mental impairment? If such a definition could be provided, it seems plausible that this would amount to a necessary condition of mental impairment. To claim otherwise would be to claim that a person could be said to be mentally impaired but to have a fully developed mind. It is not clear that this is a coherent combination of claims.

Is 'arrested development' of mind a sufficient condition of mental impairment? If one accepts that the development of one's mind may be arrested without its being the case that one is mentally impaired, it follows that arrested development cannot be a sufficient condition of mental impairment.

(ii) The term 'incomplete development of mind' also seems open to the charge of unclarity. It is not clear that one's mind could ever be completely developed; nor when or on what grounds one could make such a judgement. Can one ever say that one's mind is completely developed? It seems to me that one cannot. Given this, it follows either that one's state of mind is always incomplete, or worse that it could never be said that the development of one's mind is incomplete (i.e. since there are no criteria to determine what counts as completion of a mind).

If, for the sake of argument, these fairly serious concerns over the expression 'incomplete development of mind' are ignored, it may well be true that it comprises a necessary condition of mental impairment, even if it is one so vague that it is impossible to apply in practice. But it seems highly unlikely that incomplete development of mind could be a sufficient condition of mental impairment. Surely most, if not all of us, have minds which could be further developed.

(iii) 'Impairment of intelligence' is presumably to be cashed out in terms of performance in IQ tests. But such tests are notoriously open to criticism. For example, Lee and Morgan (1989, pp.143-4) discuss the well-known case of Jeanette, a seventeen year old woman with learning difficulties for whom sterilisation was recommended on the grounds that she had a mental age of five or six. They suggest that the concept of a mental age is methodologically dubious when applied to young women such as Jeanette (IQ tests presume agreement concerning mental age). This is due to the fact that although she may perform in the IQ tests at the level of a five or six year old, her social skills were much better than a child of that age. They write 'Jeanette may not read at all, unlike many six year olds, but she may consistently out-perform most children of that age in terms of socialisation or self-help' (1990, p.144). Such a position of scepticism concerning IQ-based criteria seems common among theorists in this area.

Apart from methodological worries concerning the viability of the concept of IQ, a philosophical question remains concerning the legitimacy of dividing individuals into categories on the basis of IQ. This is especially so when there seem good grounds to suppose that such categorisation carries implications for the moral status of such individuals - we return to discuss this issue below.

If objections stemming from concerns over the concept of intelligence are overlooked, impairment of intelligence is going to turn out to be a necessary condition of the presence of mental impairment. It is not wholly clear whether it amounts to a sufficient condition. It seems that a person may have impaired intelligence without that being serious enough to amount to mental impairment. For example, suppose a person has a problem with their short-term memory. Such a person's intelligence may be said to be impaired, but it is not the case that the person is mentally impaired in the sense of meeting the criteria set down in the Act.

(iv) The appeal to impairment of social functioning in the Act also seems open to question. It appears that 'social competence' or functioning does not straightforwardly correlate with IQ. Clarke et al. (1985) point to empirical research which suggests that persons with an IQ below 70 may still function in a way which is socially competent - as, indeed, may persons with an IQ below 50. And, one is tempted to ask, just what could impairment of social functioning amount to? Consider a person who is, say, a famous musician, or a university professor but who finds it impossibly stressful to interact with others in social contexts outside her working environment. This may be said to amount to impairment in social functioning, without its being the case that the person is mentally impaired in the sense relevant to the 1983 Act.

Our brief consideration of the term 'impairment of social functioning' indicates that this cannot be regarded as a sufficient condition of the presence of mental impairment. This is due to the plausibility of examples in which a person's social functioning is impaired and in which there is no mental impairment. It is not even clear that this is a plausible necessary condition of mental impairment since a person may be 'abnormally aggressive' but otherwise socially competent. However, if it is claimed that a person who is abnormally aggressive is, thereby, rendered socially incompetent, it may be the case that this is a necessary condition of mental impairment.

(v) The term 'abnormally aggressive' also seems beset with problems. Abnormal aggression presumes a level of aggression which is normal, and is defined in relation to that. But if a normal level of aggression is hard to define then an abnormal level will be also. It is not at all clear how one could define a normal level of aggression. Would this make reference to losing one's temper given certain types of provocation? And would losing one's temper amount to merely shouting, or extend to striking persons or, say, furniture? Also, if it is claimed that there is a normal level of aggression which is associated with mental health, it seems to follow that a person who is never (or even infrequently) aggressive is not mentally healthy. There seem very serious, perhaps insuperable difficulties here.

Abnormally aggressive behaviour seems not to be a necessary condition of mental impairment. This follows since, it seems, a person might be deemed mentally impaired on the grounds that his behaviour is 'seriously irresponsible'. And, of course, displaying abnormally aggressive behaviour is not a sufficient condition of mental impairment since persons other than those with mental impairment may act abnormally aggressively.

(vi) Similarly, understanding of the term 'seriously irresponsible' trades upon prior judgement of what constitutes responsible conduct. Deriving a workable definition of that seems highly problematic. Judgements concerning what is and what is not irresponsible conduct are heavily value-laden. Some may judge that leaving full-time employment to enter into full-time education is irresponsible conduct; others may disagree. In any event, the mere undertaking of actions judged to be seriously irresponsible does not seem to be sufficient to indicate that the actor is mentally impaired.

Unless abnormally aggressive behaviour is also classed as seriously irresponsible conduct, such conduct does not seem a plausible necessary condition of mental impairment. Nor can it be a sufficient condition since a person may behave seriously irresponsibly but not be mentally impaired. Think of persons who go climbing in Scottish mountains in the depths of winter in spite of warnings not to, or persons who go potholing in spite of forecasts of heavy rain, or a person who drinks heavily and then drives.


**Criteria for mental impairment and for intellectual disability**

One commentator, Spencer (1983), writes:

> The new terminology [i.e. of the 1983 Act] has the laudable aim of differentiating from the majority of mentally handicapped people a minority group who present particular problems which may require special management or treatment, and who may be the subject of compulsory powers. (quoted in Clarke et al., 1985, p.34)

Hence it is apparent that the 1983 Act has been interpreted in such a way that mere arrested development of mind, incomplete development of mind, impairment of intelligence, and perhaps even impairment of social functioning are not regarded as sufficient conditions of mental impairment. A person must display some combination of abnormally aggressive behaviour and seriously irresponsible conduct in order to count as mentally impaired.

More strictly, satisfaction of criteria (i)-(iv), in conjunction with satisfaction

133

of *either* (v) or (vi) (or both) is sufficient for mental impairment. And, satisfaction of any of conditions (i)-(iii) in conjunction with satisfaction of either (v) or (vi) (or both) comprise the necessary conditions of mental impairment.

What then are the criteria for the identification of intellectual disability? The following can be offered: arrested development of mind, incomplete development of mind, impairment of intelligence, and impairment of social functioning. What should be stressed is that references to abnormally aggressive behaviour or seriously irresponsible conduct cannot plausibly feature in a definition of intellectual disability since these are neither necessary nor sufficient conditions of it. It seems to follow that a definition of intellectual disability would be forced to rely wholly upon apparently theoretically dubious concepts such as 'intelligence' and 'mental development'.

As we saw, the terms arrested development of mind and incomplete development of mind are open to the charge of unclarity. Impairment of intelligence relies upon a dubiously applicable concept - that of intelligence. And impairment of social functioning seems neither to be a necessary nor a sufficient condition of intellectual disability (where, for the sake of argument, it is allowed that this can be defined by reference to IQ).

A second set of worries are more philosophical in character. Even if the concept of intelligence proves secure enough to rest a definition of intellectual disability upon it, is it plausible to hold that the apparent relationship between level of intelligence and moral status should be sustained?

One commentator, Wikler (1979) seems to argue that if such a claim is accepted, it follows that the moral status of very intelligent people should be greater than that enjoyed by averagely intelligent people. Thus, he claims, the former group could justifiably act paternalistically toward the latter group. Presumably, few will be persuaded by Wikler's suggestion. But it indicates one implication of adopting the position described above.

Also, it can be pointed out that intelligence seems not to be a property which is morally worthy in itself. It is a means towards the fulfilment of ends which are morally assessable. The fact that one has intelligence enables one to act in ways to which moral predicates can be applied - e.g. 'good', 'bad' etc. The mere fact that one is intelligent seems not to be relevant to an assessment of one's moral worth.

Further, it may be argued that emphasis on intelligence as something of high value is itself a symptom of an implausibly individualistic or atomistic view of persons; that is, of considering the abilities and deficits of persons in individualistic terms. An emphasis on the kinds of problem solving tests which are presented in IQ tests may be said to constitute evidence of this. The person is required to solve formal problems in an attempt to construct a social vacuum. An alternative approach to determination of criteria relevant to moral status might consider much more the nature of the relationship of the individual with other individuals. For example, Vanier writes:

> Handicapped people...are frequently endowed with qualities of heart which serve to remind so-called normal people that their own hearts are closed. Their simplicity frequently serves to reveal our own duplicity, untruthfulness and hypocrisy. (1976, quoted by Bayley, 1991, p.92)

The strong implication here is that the effects which individuals have on others ought to be taken into account in considerations of moral status in addition to the quality of those relations. In the context of intellectual disability such effects are typically not ones which would be taken into account in IQ tests. Relatedly, it may be pointed out that the existence of individuals with certain types of conditions provides the opportunity for what may be termed 'moral growth' (Chadwick, 1987, p.95). The suggestion seems to be that moral sensitivities and moral development may be prompted by consideration of the plight of disabled individuals.

Once more, what is being pointed to here is that it may not be legitimate to draw conclusions concerning moral status on the basis of criteria which are essentially individualistic; they are individualistic in the sense that they do not take into account the nature and the quality of the webs of relationships within which people are enmeshed (cf. Gilligan, 1982).

A second charge to which the view may be vulnerable is one of an implausible atomism. This is due to its presumption of an isolable intellectual component of a person. It can be claimed that persons are not constituted of distinct component parts but are best conceived of holistically; i.e. in the sense that persons are more than simply the sum of their parts. In support of such a claim it may be pointed out that the emotional responses evinced by a person are partially constitutive of a person's identity. And, it may be said plausibly that emotional factors may influence or affect intellectual performance. If intellectual and, say, emotional factors prove inextricable, atomism seems threatened (cf. Greaves, 1994).

In review of what has been claimed here so far: We began by considering the low moral status accorded to intellectually disabled individuals. Following consideration of the Mental Health Act 1983 it was concluded that neither seriously irresponsible nor abnormally aggressive behaviour should figure among criteria for defining intellectual disability. Insofar as a definition of that phenomenon can be provided it relies upon appeals to notions such as intelligence and intellectual development. Theorists within the field of intellectual disability seem to regard these concepts with some scepticism. In addition to this methodological worry there also remain concerns regarding the legitimacy of drawing links between intelligence and moral status.

## Why bother? Definitions and conceptions of intellectual disability

In response to these sceptical comments it might pertinently be queried whether there is any legitimacy or value in terms such as 'intellectual disability', 'mental handicap' etc. and it may be claimed that such terms should be abandoned. Hence, it may be relevant to consider the question: Why bother attempting to define 'intellectual disability' (etc.) anyway? After all, it is not the case that there is a general term to refer to all groups of individuals. For example, there is no general term to refer to people who are, say, 32, red-haired and over five feet tall, so why should there be a general term to refer to persons who are deemed to be intellectually disabled?

One motivation for classification of individuals into groups is that there may be benefits to be gained as a consequence of such classification. Crudely, suppose it is considered that reduction of the incidence of persons born with conditions associated with intellectual disability is a desirable goal. From the perspective of a person who is intellectually disabled this may be considered a good thing since it may mean limited resources available to help such persons will not be stretched further. Similarly, this may be considered a good thing from the perspective of the relatives of such people.

Also, the availability of a definition of intellectual disability may enhance the likelihood of scientific research in that area, due to its being a term which refers to recognised medical or sociological kinds. So there are at least these two ways in which it may be beneficial to have a definition of intellectual disability which individuals either meet or fail to meet.

McCullough in his paper 'The world gained and the world lost: labelling the mentally retarded' (1984) seems to go much further. He claims that those to whom the label 'mentally retarded' is legitimately applied both gain a world and lose a world as a direct consequence of the label. What is gained by the application of the label 'is the basis for an entitlement to special treatment' (1984, p.99).

McCullough proposes that the world gained, so to speak, by the label 'mentally retarded' does not have to be acquired at the expense of the world lost. The extent to which McCullough achieves this conclusion will be returned to later. But a key claim in his overall argument is that there is a need to reject 'fixed-state' definitions of intellectual disability (1984, p.104).

McCullough offers the definition of intellectual disability put forward by the American Association on Mental Deficiency (AAMD) as an example of a fixed-state definition. It includes the expression 'significantly subaverage general intellectual functioning' (McCullough, 1984, p.108). McCullough suggests that the reference to 'general intellectual functioning' here implies that one's intellectual level is at a fixed state; specifically that it is fixed at a level below that which is the norm and hence that the level of functioning that one is capable of is significantly subaverage. The suggestion is, then, that the AAMD definition of mental retardation implies that the cognitive abilities of a person labelled as 'mentally retarded' are fixed: there is no possibility of further development.

McCullough proposes that a fixed state view of 'mental retardation' be replaced by what he terms a 'process-oriented' view. The suggestion seems to be that the competencies of individuals are not fixed but are subject to change. They can increase or decrease with age and with education: one may become less able to play football as one grows older, but better able to hold one's temper. There is no reason to suppose that the interests and abilities of intellectually disabled persons remain static. Hence, a fixed state conception of such individuals seems mistaken.

An example of a process-oriented definition of intellectual disability is not offered by McCullough, nor will one be attempted here. But the negative claim that fixed state definitions be rejected seems a sound one. In order to try to say why, use can be made of the concept of competence.

The suggestion is that a fixed-state definition of intellectual disability fosters the impression that such individuals are globally incompetent: both at one time and at all future times. In contrast to a fixed-state view, a process-oriented view of intellectual functioning leaves room for the view that a person's level of functioning is not necessarily fixed. A process-oriented view allows that a person may not be competent to perform a type of task at one time but may be competent to perform it at a later time.

McCullough seems to say that adoption of a process-oriented view makes it much more likely that the question of a person's competence will not be regarded on an all-or-nothing basis. A process-oriented view allows for the possibility that incompetence in one area of function - what we might term local incompetence - need not imply global incompetence.

Further, focusing on the notion of competence may prove instructive in obtaining an adequate conception of intellectual disability. Such a focus inclines one to consider task-specificity. For, the notion of competence itself is task specific (Beauchamp and Childress, 1989, p.80). One may be competent to mend a puncture, but not competent to perform neurosurgery. So it should be accepted as uncontroversial that competence is a task-specific notion. And, it can be accepted that from the mere fact that one is not competent to perform a task of one type, it does not follow that one is thereby globally incompetent. These claims hardly seem contentious, yet they seem to be lost sight of in the context of intellectual disability.

Given the wide differences in levels of functioning in individuals described as intellectually disabled (etc.), and in the light of the pitfalls of fixed-state definitions of that condition, it may be proposed that definitions of intellectual disability which foster the conception of persons with such disabilities as globally incompetent should be rejected. Why might such a proposal be seriously considered?

First, it seems true that global definitions foster the view that if a person is intellectually disabled, then her level of functioning is across the board lower than other non-disabled members of society. And, they at least foster, and perhaps preserve, the view that if a person is intellectually disabled at a particular time, she is globally incompetent, not just at that time, but in the future also - for the remainder of the person's life in fact.

Second, as we saw in the earlier stages of this paper it is not even clear that a theoretically adequate definition of intellectual disability can be set out. IQ-based criteria seem beset with methodological problems; and behavioural criteria seem similarly beset with difficulties.[3]

Third, the very idea of positing criteria which a person must meet in order to be accredited with full moral status may be open to objection. There is a presumption in such a proposal that a particular set of actions are morally preferable to another set. By itself, this is not objectionable: it is indeed plausible that we can judge some ways of acting to be morally preferable to others. But what are the types of actions by virtue of which a person is classed as intellectually disabled? They are certainly not ones which involve direct harms to others or to such persons themselves - i.e. otherwise they would be subject to the conditions of the 1983 Act.

Fourth, in the care of persons deemed intellectually disabled certain trends or approaches to be implemented in regimes of care arise. One such widely-known and adopted approach derives from the work of Wolfensberger (1983) and accords great weight to the concept of normalisation. The approach emphasises the importance of intellectually disabled people behaving in ways which are congruent with those dominant in the society in which they live. In accordance with this approach, it is proposed that people with such disabilities should engage in activities which are 'Age- and Culture-appropriate' (Wolfensberger, 1983, p.237). Age-appropriateness, here, appears to signify chronological age.

Consideration of the following case example, however, generates serious concern about acceptance of any such general care strategy as that proposed by Wolfensberger. The example is one recounted to the author by a person employed in the care of persons with quite serious intellectual disabilities. It involved a woman, B, aged 28 who displayed behaviour which was considered age-inappropriate by many staff employed in her care. B liked to carry a doll around with her wherever she went. Of course, this behaviour prompted some strange looks from other members of the public and the occasional comment. From the perspective of normalisation it seems plain that B should not be permitted to carry her doll around - at least in public places. But when her carers tried to persuade B to leave the doll behind on her trips out, she refused. Various strategies were employed to try to change B's behaviour but none was successful. The person who related this case example claimed that attempts to persuade B to leave her doll behind before going out were quite intense and B became upset and distressed during these interactions. A minority view among the staff at B's home held that B should not be prevented from taking her doll out if that was what she wanted to do.

The relevance of this example from the perspective of the global/local contrast should be fairly clear: adoption of a global view implies that B's decision to take the doll with her cannot have been a competent one. And, if it is agreed that a normalisation policy is to be implemented in regimes of care for intellectually disabled people, then again, it seems that B should be coerced into leaving the doll behind. Adoption of a local view of competence implies that it should first be determined whether B's decision to carry the doll with her is a competent one, and a decision concerning what to do next should await the outcome of that question.

It may be added that, in general, it seems to be the case that citizens who make decisions concerning their own behaviour for themselves have those decisions respected. If this consideration is applied to the case of B, providing her decision to carry the doll around is a competent one, it seems difficult to justify preventing her from so doing. And on some criteria of justified paternalism, whether or not B's decision is competent it was not justifiable to remove her doll.

Our recent considerations are intended to motivate abandonment of the employment of general terms to apply to intellectually disabled persons which encourage the view that such persons are globally incompetent. This last claim may be vulnerable to at least one objection. It stems from McCullough's suggestion that although there is a world lost to individuals deemed intellectually disabled, there is also a world gained. Recall that for McCullough application of the label 'mentally retarded' to an individual 'is the basis for an entitlement to special treatment' (1984, p.99).

But McCullough's claims for a world gained can be responded to. First, it is clear of course that the appeals to a world gained are merely metaphorical: humans all inhabit the same world. Second, and more important, it is simply not true that the label 'mentally retarded' bestows upon an individual entitlements to special allowances. Even if it is accepted that this is the case for intellectually disabled persons in the USA, it is certainly not the case for intellectually disabled persons in other countries. Think of a country such as Romania under the reign of President Ceausescu, and extremely poor countries in which there are no welfare provisions for citizens. There seems to be no world gained in such places for those deemed intellectually disabled. Even in the UK, certain social benefits may be due to intellectually disabled persons, but these benefits are often difficult to obtain, and are only accessible to those with articulate parents or guardians. It is true that there is employment legislation in the UK the purpose of which is to ensure that employers take on a percentage of persons who are registered as disabled. But it is far from clear that employers honour these obligations (Bayles, 1985).

A further possible reason for maintaining general terms such as 'mental handicap' etc. may be that, as mentioned earlier, it encourages the identification of a clear research area for medical scientists. But I do not think this a plausible move. First, the types of disabilities which are associated with intellectual disability are so varied, it is not clear that they form a homogeneous group. One person might be profoundly physically disabled, and severely cognitively disabled to the extent of being completely unaware of her environment. Another person may have no physical disabilities, but have an IQ which is between 65 and 75 - only slightly below the normal range. Given such wide disparity in the capabilities of persons labelled intellectually disabled it can seem arbitrary to apply a general term to that group of people. Also, it is unlikely that medical scientists research into 'intellectual disability'; rather, research topics are more fine-grained - i.e. into specific syndromes and conditions. Given that these syndromes and conditions would retain their integrity due to their association with specific kinds of physical structures, there is no reason to suppose that abandonment of the term 'intellectual disability' will entail cessation of research into conditions associated with such disability.


**Conclusion: conditions of adequacy**

Finally, if the above considerations are accepted, it may prove possible to posit at least five conditions of adequacy concerning a definition of intellectual disability (etc.). First, any such definition should not be a fixed-state definition. Clearly, the abilities of people with disabilities are not necessarily static. Second, a proposed definition should avoid making global claims concerning the competence of the relevant individuals. As we have heard, competence is a task-specific notion and global judgements concerning competence seem hard to warrant. Third, following on from the first two proposed conditions any definition should encourage emphasis upon local competencies. Fourth, if the considerations offered earlier concerning an objectionable individualism are accepted, then criteria for the definition of intellectual disability (etc.) should take into account nonindividualistic considerations (e.g. the individual's place in a web of social relations). Fifth, and finally, for reasons given earlier, any definition should avoid commitment to cognitive atomism.

## Notes

1. The term 'intellectually disabled' is intended here to refer to the same individuals otherwise referred to by terms such as 'mentally handicapped', 'mentally retarded', or individuals with 'learning difficulties', and so on. I will use 'intellectual disabilities' and 'mental disabilities' as synonyms.

2. It is worth noting that in England and Wales between 1 October 1988 and 1 October 1992, of 1613 women who were informed that their foetus had Down's Syndrome, 1488 opted for termination of pregnancy - just under 90% of cases (Morris et al., 1994).

3. The adoption of Adaptive Behaviour Scales has proved problematic (McCullough, 1984, pp.110-111; Clarke et al., 1985, p.45). Further, there are general philosophical problems in attempting to derive conclusions regarding mental capacity from behavioural criteria. Suppose behaviours of type B are taken to constitute adaptive behaviours. It is evident that these could be undertaken in the absence of relevant mental states (e.g. by coincidence, or by an android) so behaviours of type B are not a sufficient condition for the presence of the relevant mental states. And, a person who is completely paralysed may well still be intelligent, hence behaviours of type B are not a necessary condition of the presence of relevant mental states.

## Bibliography

Baldwin, S. and Hattersley, J. (eds) (1991), *Mental Handicap: Social Science Perspectives*, Routledge, London.

Bayles, M.D. (1985), 'Equal human rights and employment for mentally retarded persons', in Laura and Ashman (eds) (1985), pp.11-27.

Bayley, M. (1991), 'Normalisation or social role valorization: an adequate philosophy?', in Baldwin and Hattersley (eds) (1991), pp.87-99.

Beauchamp, T.L. and Childress, J.F. (1989), *Principles of Biomedical Ethics*, 3rd edition, Oxford University Press, Oxford.

Benjamin, M. and Curtis, J. (1986), *Ethics in Nursing*, Oxford University Press, Oxford.

Chadwick, R. (ed.) (1987), *Ethics, Reproduction and Genetic Control*, Routledge, London.

Clarke, A.M., Clarke, A.D.B. and Berg, J.M. (1985), *Mental Deficiency*, 4th edition, Methuen, London.

*Diagnostic and Statistical Manual of Mental Disorders DSM-III-R*, (1987), 3rd edition, American Psychiatric Association, Washington.

Gilligan, C. (1982), *In a Different Voice*, Harvard University Press, London.

Greaves, D. (1994), 'The historical conceptualisation of impaired capacity and some ethical implications', unpublished manuscript.

Harris, J. (1985), *The Value of Life*, Routledge and Kegan Paul, London.

Hattersley, J. (1991), 'The future of normalisation', in Baldwin and Hattersley (eds) (1991), pp.1-11.

Heaton-Ward, W.A. and Wiley, Y. (1984), *Mental Handicap*, 5th edition, Wright, Bristol.

Kopelman, L. (1984), 'Respect and the retarded: issues of valuing and labeling', in Kopelman and Moskop (eds) (1984), pp.65-86.

Kopelman, L. and Moskop, J.C. (eds) (1984), *Ethics and Mental Retardation*, Reidel, Dordrecht.

Kuhse, H. and Singer, P. (1985), *Should the Baby Live? The Problem of Handicapped Infants*, Oxford University Press, Oxford.

Laura, R.S. and Ashman, A.F. (eds), 1985, *Moral Issues in Mental Retardation*, Croom Helm, London.

Lee, R. and Morgan, D. (1989), 'A lesser sacrifice? Sterilization and mentally handicapped women', in Lee and Morgan (eds) (1989), *Birthrights, Law and Ethics at the Beginnings of Life*, Routledge, London, pp.132-154.

Mason, J.K. and McCall Smith, R.A. (1994), *Law and Medical Ethics*, 4th edition, Butterworths, London.

McCullough, L.B. (1984), 'The world gained and the world lost: labeling the mentally retarded', in Kopelman and Moscop (eds) (1984), pp.99-118.

Morris, J.K., Mutton, D.E., Ide, R., Alberman, E. and Bobrow, M. (1994), 'Monitoring trends in prenatal diagnosis of Down's syndrome in England and Wales, 1989-92', *Journal of Medical Screening*, 1, pp.233-37.

Spencer, D. (1983), 'Classification of "severe mental impairment"', *Mental Handicap*, 11, p.174.

Tierney, A.J. (ed.) (1983), *Nurses and the Mentally Handicapped*, Wiley, Chichester.

Todd, F.J. (1967), *Social Work with the Mentally Subnormal*, Routledge and Kegan Paul, London.

Wikler, D. (1979), 'Paternalism and the mildly retarded', *Philosophy and Public Affairs*, Vol. 8, No. 4, pp.377-92.

Wolfensberger, W. (1983), 'Social role valorization: a proposed new term for the prinicple of normalization', *Mental Retardation*, Vol. 21, No. 6, pp.234-39.

# Part Three
# HEALTH POLICY

# 9 Justice and health care

*Hugh Upton*

## Introduction

To start in very general terms, justice is often said to be a matter of people receiving what is due to them, where this has two sub-divisions: the rectification of previous acts of injustice and the fair distribution of goods. It leads naturally to at least two other concepts. Firstly, justice is thought to be connected with rights, though perhaps in different ways in the two divisions. To take rectification, we may think that criminals get what is due to them when they are punished, though most will think it strange to say that they have a right to punishment, given that it is not an option for them but an imposition by others. Unless we understand punishment as a kind of penance (on which possibility see Duff, 1986) we will think that the right is to punish, not to be punished. On the other hand, when we come to consider the fair distribution of goods and services we are likely to speak of some recipient's entitlement or right to a fair allocation. Secondly, thoughts of justice also lead to the concept of desert, which raises different issues again. That you deserve something is one possible reason why it may be due to you, but since we tend to think of desert as arising from personal qualities or achievements (whether good or bad) its relevance to questions of justice is bound to be controversial. The connection may seem clear in the case of rectification, yet it can be disputed whether wrongdoers deserve punishment. In the case of distributive justice, some will see desert as relevant on the grounds that some conditions are self-inflicted and thus not deserving of assistance from public funds, while others will see this branch of justice as aiming to alleviate poverty regardless of individual desert.

To focus on distributive justice, we can begin by identifying the elements of one familiar tradition. Firstly, that a state has a duty to monitor the condition of its citizens and to ensure that no individual falls below a certain level of welfare. Secondly, that health has a distinct status within welfare, not one simply to be subsumed under the relief of poverty. Health, that is, is regarded as a special value (discussed in Daniels, 1985) requiring the supply of health care to be free or subsidised for all. Thirdly, it is held that we should not look too closely at whether someone's poverty or ill-health are self-inflicted. Whether this restraint is simply an acknowledgement of the difficulty of discovering the extent to which people choose their fate, or is based on the idea that it is irrelevant in these circumstances even if it is discoverable, there is certainly a widespread belief that any state has a duty to offer all its citizens assistance in avoiding poor health and extreme deprivation. Fourthly, that this policy will be understood as giving the citizens a right to such assistance. That is, even if the exact level was negotiable, assistance of some kind could be claimed rather than accepted as charity, so that a wrong would be done to the would-be recipient were it to be withheld.

At least two challenges are offered to these views. One, mentioned already, is the idea that a person's behaviour is always relevant, in that while the state should respond to misfortune it has no duty to rescue people from the consequences of their own negligent or foolish behaviour. In other words it is felt that the contribution made by a person's well-informed and freely chosen actions to their own distressed condition will reduce their right, if not of access to resources, then at least to their free provision. This view has often been heard where poverty is concerned and is increasingly voiced in matters of health.

There is, though, a much more radical challenge to the idea of the public provision of health and welfare services, one that has had great influence in recent years and which will therefore be the main concern of this essay. This is the idea that it is no part of the function of a state to supply these services at all, so that the difficult question of whether they are needed as a result of bad luck or bad judgement does not even arise. Furthermore, the argument is not the common one concerning the alleged inefficiency of state provision but one that claims that the state simply cannot have such a function because it lacks the moral right to use resources for these purposes. So, efficient or not, private provision is all we can permit on this view if we are to avoid infringing people's basic moral rights.

This view, part of the doctrine usually referred to as libertarianism, is best studied through the particularly forceful version provided by Robert Nozick in *Anarchy, State, and Utopia* (Nozick, 1974), a work that presents us with a profoundly different account of distributive justice to that which many of us take for granted in the welfare state. We cannot, however, plunge straight into the issue of distribution since one of the aims (and virtues) of libertarian thought is to draw our attention to the status of the things that are distributed. How does the state come by them? Are they already owned or are they unattached and free to be given away? In short, we must begin with the idea of property.

## The foundation of property rights

Our ownership of anything seems to be constituted by our rights against others that what is done with it is a matter for our decision and control. These rights, naturally enough, are usually taken to be legal ones, but our concern here will be with moral rights, with whether we can discover anything that might justify what is enacted and enforced by law. One of the classic enquiries into the moral foundations of property rights can be found in a work of the late seventeenth century, John Locke's *Two Treatises of Government* (Locke, 1960, second treatise, chapter 5). Of great interest in itself it is especially important here as a significant influence on recent libertarian thinking, particularly that of Nozick. In an attempt to clarify the idea, Locke asks us to consider how property could come about in the first instance, before any question of its legitimate transfer to someone else arises; in fact, before it could possibly arise, since I cannot legitimately give or sell what is not mine already. In brief, Locke's account of the matter is as follows.

Initially the world was given by God to mankind in common. It was thus, for Locke, strictly not unowned but owned by all as common land, such that all had an equal right to use any of it. Unsurprisingly, God's right of ownership is unquestioned. The problem for Locke is that of how individual private property can arise from this gift of common ownership, of how anyone can justly exclude others from some particular piece of land and alone decide what is to be done with it. His solution is to appeal to something he seems to regard as self-evident, namely that we all have property rights over our own persons and our own labour. One effect of this, in his view, is that when we use our labour on what is held in common, whether by tilling the soil, gathering fruit or hunting wild animals, we add something that we already own (our labour) to these items and hence acquire property rights over the items themselves. Thus, provided we are not wasteful, and have left enough of the same quality for others, we have the right, for example, to enclose as private property for our sole use a part of what was formerly common land.

For Locke, then, property in external things is to be explained by something morally basic, the private property rights we all have over ourselves. There is no need to go further into the details and obscurities of this account here, since what matters to us, and indeed to a whole tradition of political thought, is the general principle that property is ultimately to be explained by our self-ownership. This is not, of course, the only kind of argument in support of private property (for others see Becker, 1977) but it is the kind appropriate to libertarianism and the kind apparently favoured by Nozick. The other common form of argument, the appeal to useful consequences (exemplified by the familiar claim that the possibility of acquiring property is a vital incentive for initiative and thus for economic growth) is clearly of a quite different sort, and one that is most unlikely to support such powerful rights (absolute in all but name) as we find in libertarianism.


## The libertarian theory


In *Anarchy, State, and Utopia* we find that Nozick, like Locke (and doubtless like most of the rest of us) assumes that we have rights to private property, rights that have a moral foundation distinct from their legal recognition. Of course, it is too much to expect that all the recognised property holdings will be morally legitimate. The conditions of original acquisition (whether Locke's or some other version) may have been violated, or there may since have been unfair transfers of what was justly acquired. The assumption, though, is that just ownership is at least possible and that attempts can be made to rectify past injustices. Given this, Nozick then in effect asks two things of us. Firstly, that we take these property rights seriously, accepting that if something really is mine then no-one can legitimately take it from me without my consent. Secondly, that we take people's freedom seriously, accepting that, within the usual constraint of not harming others, I can do with my property as I please, which includes giving it away or offering it for sale. The problem is that while both these points may strike us as perfectly reasonable in themselves, they seem to lead to conclusions that many will find alarming. One, which appears to follow straightforwardly, is that just as no private individual may take another's money and use it to buy health care for the poor, nor may a government do so. In other words, improving the health of the needy by the coercive redistribution of resources through taxation is prohibited on the libertarian view. The other (Nozick, pp.160-4) is that if we uphold the idea of freedom of transfer then any attempt by a government to redistribute wealth according to some desired pattern is always liable to be undermined by private acts of giving or selling. For example, suppose an egalitarian government had actually succeeded in equalising everyone's wealth, it could then only preserve this pattern of distribution by preventing private transfers, or at least by immediately stepping in to redress the balance every time one occurred. Nozick assumes, reasonably enough, that this is unacceptable. Libertarians, on the other hand, have no need to worry about who transfers what to whom, provided that the transactions are conducted fairly, since in their view just transfers cannot possibly create an unjust distribution. In fact, Nozick claims (p.151) they are bound to preserve justice, in that if we start with a just distribution and allow only just transfers we must be left with a just distribution.

There are, then, three elements in Nozick's theory of justice, those of original acquisition, transfer, and the rectification of any injustice in the first two. It should be clear how this differs from what is more usually understood as distributive justice. While the egalitarian, for example, will look at the current pattern of distribution of goods, services and opportunities and on this basis draw conclusions regarding the changes to the pattern that justice requires, the libertarian will insist that we look instead at the history of the current pattern, at the legitimacy or otherwise of the acts of acquisition and transfer that led to its existence. Then, once we have as far as possible corrected any acts of theft, coercion and trickery that have marred this process, this will be the whole business of distributive justice attended to, since, as far as we can ensure it, everyone will have all and only that to which they are entitled. It would on this view be absurd even to ask any further questions about how goods should be distributed in society, for there is nothing further to consider. Hence, for a government to interfere in any other way would be for it to violate people's rights, since it would be to interfere with people's free choices regarding their own property. Coercive taxation for health care is simply one such violation. If we are entitled to our money then it is ours to do with as we please, and only if we are not entitled to it should anyone be taking it away from us.

It is worth standing back a little at this point to take a broader view of Nozick's state and its functions. His calling it the 'minimal state' is obviously apt, there being a strict moral limit on the range of functions that a state may perform. It must protect its citizens from the use of illegitimate force, establish law and its enforcement within its boundaries, and thereby uphold the citizens' rights to freedom from undue interference with their lives and property. This accomplished, the state's work is complete.

Two obvious questions arise here: why are these functions allowed and why are other functions forbidden? On the first, the answer seems to lie in the very reason for the existence of a state at all. In Nozick's view a state can arise quite legitimately out of the reasonable, self-interested desires of a group of individuals for a secure and ordered life. They are, after all, quite likely to decide that the best defence against insecurity and disorder is to organise themselves, and to set up a body with a monopoly of law, judicial process and the just use of force in their region, and such an organisation is exactly what Nozick's state amounts to. It is possible, of course, that there will be anarchists who want no state at all but anyone who does want one will surely expect it to perform these minimal functions and can thus be expected to support their maintenance.

Why then can the state have no further role, such as that of ensuring some minimum level of health care for all its citizens? Part of Nozick's answer, that this would violate people's property rights, has already been given, but it is vital to look at the reasons underlying this claim, the reasons that form the foundation of his theory. As we have seen, Nozick is above all concerned with people's rights, where these are taken to be of a negative kind, rights against the interference by others with ourselves and our property. Further, they are of great strength. Nozick calls them side-constraints, in that they set rigid boundaries to what we may do, and they may reasonably be interpreted as absolute. (The possibility of weaker versions will be considered in the next section.) They must not be violated even for the most worthy of other ends. Clearly, then, it is reasonable to ask why these negative rights should have such a privileged status, one that excludes any diminution for gains elsewhere. Nozick's response is to appeal to the importance of freedom, to the idea that people must not simply be used against their will for the benefit of others but must be left with the freedom of choice that is essential if their lives are to have meaning for them. The success of this appeal will be considered later.

Having outlined Nozick's theory it is perhaps as well to warn against dismissing it too quickly. Naturally an argument to the effect that the National Health Service is immoral arouses strong feelings, but the philosophical concern must be with whether it is correct and, if we think not, to present the most effective objection we can find. One characteristic response is simply to reject the argument by rejecting its conclusion. If an argument has the conclusion that there may be no injustice in a society with great extremes of wealth and welfare, where some are ill and destitute and others pampered by costly private health care, then, it may be said, the argument *must* be wrong. Yet however sympathetic one may feel with such a response the fact remains that it will not impress the libertarians. Nozick, for one, knew that his view would challenge our preconceptions about justice and put it forward in that spirit.

Another common reaction is to regard the theory as nothing but individual self-interest projected on a grand scale at the inevitable expense of those least able to help themselves. Yet here the libertarian can point out that if this charge is not one of injustice, but simply a concern for the condition of the needy, nothing in the minimal state will prevent its citizens from doing something about it. All health care professionals will be free to give some of their services for nothing, just as other citizens will be free to donate money to a medical fund for the destitute. The libertarian claim is only that no-one, including the government, has the right to force us to do these things. In other words, the theory does not itself endorse a selfish outlook; it does not demand disparities of wealth nor insist that people look solely to their own well-being, but merely sets limits to what governments may do to counter such tendencies.

Finally there is a temptation to object to the practical difficulties of Nozick's account of justice, to point to the likely impossibility of discovering the truth about successive transfers (even of land alone) since the time of original acquisition. This, it is true, is an important and interesting problem but it may not be the best objection to Nozick. Firstly, it is a problem for anyone who believes in property rights and the possibility of their transfer, none of whom will be particularly happy with a situation of agnosticism, knowing that things may be owned by someone but with no idea whom. Though this might turn out to be the case, an objection that is specific to Nozick would be preferable here. Secondly, if we rely on the case for agnosticism Nozick could reply by admitting the practical problem but assuming our agreement with him in principle as to what counts as justice in distribution. This is surely unsatisfactory. If we feel a disquiet about this account of justice, it goes deeper than the problem of the obscurity of history. It lies in the feeling that there must be weaknesses in the foundations of the theory itself. Two such weaknesses will be considered here, the first arising from a more critical look at the idea of property rights and the second from questioning whether an appeal to the value of freedom really supports the idea of the minimal state.

## The extent of property rights

Given the general libertarian claim that the world's resources, far from being unattached and awaiting distribution, are owned by absolute right, it is important to note that this degree of strength of ownership does not follow from the idea of property itself. We are after all quite familiar with the fact that property rights can exist without holding equally against all persons (since the government may insist on purchasing our property where private individuals may not) and without holding in all respects (since we can own listed buildings without having a right to demolish them). Despite such limitations the idea seems to remain a coherent and useful one and there seems no reason why this should not be so in its moral as well as legal use. However, although this shows that weaker forms are possible the questions remain of whether our moral right to property is indeed a side-constraint of the kind Nozick proposes, and of whether such strong rights can be justified. Naturally we cannot consider all extant arguments, but we can look at the sort described earlier as likely to be useful to libertarianism and perhaps draw some conclusions of general relevance.

It is thus appropriate at this point to return to Locke's question of how private property could justly arise in the first place, a question that is crucial to the legitimacy of all the later transfers of rights that we tend to take for granted. Can we make use of the idea of self-ownership (see Day, 1966; Waldron, 1988) or at least ownership of our labour, abilities and skills, to show how parts of the world become privately owned? Suppose we consider land, historically the most important source of wealth, and imagine someone discovering an area that is unclaimed, starting to work on it and eventually living off it. For what reason, if any, might we think that they come to have exclusive property rights over the land? Locke's view was that under certain circumstances the mixing of the already owned labour with the land was sufficient to produce these rights. It is a view, though, that seems to raise problems rather than provide a solution. Even if we pass over the obscurity of mixing something intangible with the soil, there is still the question of exactly why this process should generate exclusive moral rights over something. As Nozick himself points out (pp.174-5) it is as easy to see it as a way of losing our labour as of gaining the land.

Rather than pursue this further we can turn to an argument which, while in broadly the same tradition, is generally found more compelling. It is the claim that the person who has laboured on the unowned land deserves to have it. It is their labour that has been applied (where this is to be understood not just as distinguishing it from other labour, but as attributing ownership) so naturally, it might be said, the land becomes their property. In support of this, appeal might be made to the idea that making an effort where others do not must give us some moral advantage, some better claim than others have to the product. Can these two elements support such a claim, and not only a better claim than others have but one that generates the side-constraints of libertarianism? We can approach these questions by first asking how an argument based on desert differs from the one used by Locke.

Consider for a moment just the first element, that I would deserve to own the land because in working on it I would have used something that I already owned, namely my labour. This version resembles Locke's in assuming the prior existence of ownership, but differs from his in the way my rights are extended. The idea here is that my pre-existing property rights provide a reason for my having rights over the land, not that my current property mingles with the soil so as to render it mine also, which is what Locke had in mind. Yet although the new version seems more plausible than Locke's I do not think that on any interpretation it will explain how absolute property rights could be morally justified. One difficulty is plain if we recall the initial definition of property as comprising someone's rights against others to control what is done with something. If we apply this to my ownership of my labour we must ask how it is that my right to be left free to use my labour in a certain way, in this case to work on a piece of land, could result in permanent moral rights over the land, rights that are so strong that unless I decide otherwise there could be no other claim on it or its products, no matter who the claimant is, or what their condition of health, handicap or welfare. There seems no reason to suppose that my right to choose what I do with my labour creates such powerful rights of ownership. Then there is also a difficulty with the premise of the argument, for we can always go back a stage and ask whether the ownership of my labour is plausibly thought of as morally absolute. Could there never be a legitimate claim on that either?

Let us then add the second element of the desert argument, namely the deserving nature of people who make an effort and actually do some labouring. That is, we will explicitly add the idea of desert to the premise of the argument, so that we start from the assumption that people not only own their labour but are also worthy or deserving in so far as they make some use of it. Can we now conclude that they acquire exclusive property rights over that which they work on? Again, surely, there is a gap in the argument. However deserving the effort, it will be ineffectual without the assortment of abilities, skills and capacities involved in its application to some project. So the question of the status of these must also arise. Are they deserved, and so fully as to provide the foundation of absolute property rights? Clearly not. Much of the complex mixture of character, intelligence, skill and physical capacity that makes up someone's personal contribution to an enterprise is either fortuitously inherited or derived from the work and care of others, which is hardly suggestive of our fully deserving it. It is a matter of luck, not merit. Thus even if there was some argument from deserved abilities to deserved property, it could scarcely justify absolute property rights over the whole product.

It is worth noting here that this issue of the nature and extent of our rights over our productive capacities is fundamental, such that different answers here will lead to quite different accounts of distributive justice. For example, in John Rawls' *Theory of Justice* (Rawls, 1972) we find that weight is to be given to the principle that 'undeserved inequalities call for redress' and that 'since inequalities of birth and natural endowment are undeserved, these inequalities are to be somehow compensated for' (Rawls, p.100). Indeed, he regards one element of his theory as representing 'in effect, an agreement to regard the distribution of natural talents as a common asset and to share in the benefits of this distribution whatever it turns out to be' (p.101). Yet these and other possibilities (on which see Kymlicka, 1990) are only open to us if the libertarian arguments are mistaken.

To return to these arguments, it may need emphasising that none of the foregoing scepticism regarding the arguments for property should be taken as denying that the labourer's work may give him a strong claim to the product, or at least to a large portion of it. This can simply be left as an open question. The aim has been to cast doubts on the most likely form of argument for absolute property rights. Nor is it perverse to concentrate on absolute rights in this way, for they constitute a barrier of great significance that libertarians do well to try to defend, there being no obvious principled position to fall back on if it gives way. Nozick himself (1974, p.30, footnote) is understandably wary of directly discussing whether the rights really are absolute. To illustrate the problem, suppose he made what appears to be merely a modest concession to the effect that a counter-claim against property owners is justified if it is from someone suffering complete destitution as a result of a chronic illness for which they bear no responsibility at all. Two kinds of awkward questions arise immediately for the libertarian. Firstly, is it the function of the state to enforce this kind of minimal claim to redistributive assistance? Secondly, if this claim is to be upheld in some way, why not uphold at least some claim from those suffering, say, only severe hardship resulting from an illness for the onset of which they had some slight responsibility? In respect of both variables in the second question, the degree of distress and the degree of responsibility, a criterion for assistance that is not morally arbitrary will be very elusive, and the apparent certainty of the negative side-constraints is likely to seem all the more attractive to the libertarian.

Attractive or not, though, the conclusion proposed here is that these side-constraints lack justification. We have no reason to suppose that morally absolute property rights could be established in the first place and hence none to suppose that such rights could be acquired by transfer. If this is correct we can deny that the redistributive taxation needed for a public health service is bound to violate our moral rights to property.


**Freedom**

As mentioned earlier there is another strand to Nozick's argument for the minimal state and thus against the idea of a public health service. To deal with it we have to recall the general nature of our basic rights in his theory, those rights we have simply in virtue of being persons, independently of any particular choices and agreements we may make. For Nozick they are negative, not demanding that we do anything for others but only that we refrain from interfering with them by way of harm or unjustified coercion. Now the great advantage of the minimal state, it is claimed, is that it alone respects these rights and in so doing is unique in preserving people's freedom to live their lives as they choose, unhindered by others. Of course, the state must punish all serious violations of rights, but apart from these basic negative rights of non-interference this policy will involve enforcing only those obligations that people have chosen to take on through voluntary contracts and agreements. Thus the state could force you, for example, to contribute to others' health care only if you had freely contracted to do so, thereby creating a right for someone else, and were refusing to keep to the terms of the contract.

Such a radical rejection of the received wisdom in moral and political thinking stands in need of some rationale, and Nozick's (1974, pp.48-51) can be outlined very briefly. It is that only this moral framework will grant people the freedom that is essential if they are to plan their lives in accordance with their own conception of how they want to lead them. In turn, to be guided by their own conception is essential if, as free, rational creatures, they are to be able to regard their lives as having meaning. It is thus with an appeal to human freedom and the conditions for a meaningful life that we reach the moral basis of Nozick's political theory. The property rights considered earlier, while not regarded as in need of justification in terms of beneficial consequences (Nozick, p.177), are clearly intended to fit this general picture of a set of negative rights that are above all conducive to human freedom.

As was said earlier, the most effective criticism of this account will be internal to it, bringing to light the problems it faces even on its own terms rather than simply objecting to its consequences. In this spirit there are at least two lines of thought that might be taken up here. One is the tension between the right to property and the appeal to freedom, since while property may well increase the freedom of the owner it does so precisely in virtue of constraining others. Hence the idea that absolute property rights are consistent with the ultimate appeal to the value of freedom is a matter that needs to be argued, not assumed (see Ryan, 1976; Cohen, 1979). However, rather than continuing with the specific issue of property it will be more useful to look briefly at a problem for a different part of the account, the argument concerning our need for freedom.

To assess this argument we can take the case of the provision of health care in the minimal state. The idea is that the various health care professionals will sell their services when and where they wish and that people will buy them on the same terms; standardly, no doubt, through (freely chosen) private insurance schemes. What, though, of those who are both poor and ill, who could not afford the market insurance rates and cannot now afford treatment? It is true, let us assume, that no-one is interfering with their lives or taking their property, and in this respect they may be equal in freedom to the wealthiest in the land. However, there seems to be something else of relevance here. If we consider the options open to them, the range of significant choices they are able to carry out, they are undoubtedly subject to far greater limitations than the wealthy. In other words, there seem to be two aspects to our idea of freedom (see MacCallum, 1967) and while lack of interference may be important so may our capacity to make use of the resulting liberty. Certainly interference may constrain people but so, surely, may poverty and illness, and some argument is needed to show why in the name of freedom the state should attend fully to the first kind of constraint and not at all to the second. It is a question that is particularly pressing given that Nozick's view depends ultimately on the idea of planning for a meaningful life, since it can hardly be denied that illness is typically a hindrance to such plans.

How might libertarians respond? One reply would be to point out that while many things, including illness, may harm and constrain us, only people violate our rights, and to assert that the only proper concern of the state is these violations. However, although it is surely correct that persons are the only possible violators of rights, the reply as a whole seems ineffective. Firstly, we often regard ourselves as morally responsible in part for what we allow to happen to others as well as for what we do to them, so that even if we agreed that allowing things to happen did not infringe people's basic rights we might still suppose that the state could take an interest in these events in the cause of human freedom. More generally, the reply overlooks the fact that if the final appeal is to individual freedom then the special place accorded to rights becomes open to question. So, while upholding negative rights may promote freedom, so might other interventions that conflict with such rights. For example, supposing we thought that taxation did violate our rights, it would still be true that the resulting public health service increased the freedom of those who would not otherwise have received health care.

Secondly, even if we were convinced of the special place of rights, the nature of these rights is also open to debate. Why should we accept that they are only negative? Instead, like Locke (who was thus not a libertarian) we might argue that the needy who lack means of their own have a right to the surplus of others (Locke, 1960, first treatise, ch.4, section 42). This of course is simply to raise a possibility, not to decide the issue, but it is enough for the immediate purpose. It serves as a reminder that questions both of what rights we have and of whether they override other considerations are arguable and notoriously controversial. They certainly do not provide a settled and uncontentious basis for a political theory, or for the supply of health care.


## Conclusion

Nozick did a service to political thought in asking us to take seriously the moral claim people have to be left to do as they wish with both their lives and property, not least because to take it seriously is a requirement for really understanding it, and understanding it is of direct relevance to many of the decisions being made in practical politics. Thus, although the foregoing discussion has been at an abstract level, many of the slogans being used in recent British politics (for example, that we must aim to reduce government intervention, increase freedom of choice and give back to the people more of what is theirs) take us straight to the problems we have been looking at. In other words, the success or otherwise of the libertarian arguments is of great pragmatic importance, since the very same arguments are used not only to defend the abstract ideal of a minimal state but also the actual practice of reducing state spending. Thus even if our concerns are practical ones, we cannot avoid the abstract questions. Is everyone's freedom of choice increased by cuts in public spending? Do we know that what is taken in taxation, or even the rest of what we earn, is wholly ours by some strong moral right?

The treatment of such large issues in this essay has necessarily been brief. The hope is that sufficient reasons have been given for denying the libertarian claim that states lack the right to provide a publicly funded health service, and thus also for questioning the common arguments for the reduction of state involvement in health care. Of course, just to give reasons for scepticism about absolute property rights, and about any straightforward connection between reducing public spending and increasing people's freedom, is to leave a lot to be done. To show that property rights are not so strong as obviously to overwhelm claims of need is not to show exactly why and to what extent we should respond to need. Likewise, to show that if we attend only to negative rights we may thereby permit great restrictions on many people's freedom is not to show the degree to which this should be remedied. It is important, though, given the currency of the libertarian arguments, to see that the questions of these responses and remedies have not been successfully ruled out in advance. Indeed, if we care about people's freedom, they are precisely the ones we should be considering.

### Bibliography

Becker, L.C. (1977), *Property Rights: Philosophic Foundations*, Routledge and Kegan Paul, Boston.

Cohen, G.A. (1979), 'Capitalism, freedom and the proletariat', in Ryan, A. (ed.), *The Idea of Freedom*, Oxford University Press, Oxford.

Daniels, N. (1985), *Just Health Care*, Cambridge University Press, Cambridge.

Day, J.P. (1966), 'Locke on property', *The Philosophical Quarterly*, Vol. 16, pp.207-20.

Duff, R.A. (1986), *Trials and Punishments*, Cambridge University Press, Cambridge.

Kymlicka, W. (1990), *Contemporary Political Philosophy: An Introduction*, Clarendon Press, Oxford.

Locke, J. (1960), *Two Treatises of Government*, Laslett, P. (ed.), Cambridge University Press, Cambridge.

MacCallum, G.C. (1967), 'Negative and positive freedom', *The Philosophical Review*, Vol. 76, pp.312-34.

Nozick, R. (1974), *Anarchy, State, and Utopia*, Basil Blackwell, Oxford.

Rawls, J. (1972), *A Theory of Justice*, Clarendon Press, Oxford.

Ryan, C.C. (1976), 'Yours, mine, and ours: property rights and individual liberty', *Ethics*, Vol. 87, pp.126-41.

Waldron, J. (1988), *The Right to Private Property*, Clarendon Press, Oxford.

# 10 The limits of health care

*Donald Evans*

## Introduction

Before the days of metrication it was said that 'You can't get a quart out of a pint pot'. In these post-metrication times the same is true howsoever we designate the problem. Where there is a shortage of supply and apparently endless calls for goods some of the latter will inevitably remain unmet. It would appear that this is most painfully true in the area of health care provision. It is often expressed as a practical problem in the form that limited resources cannot meet unlimited demand. Whether this is a genuine problem in health care provision is something we should ask. We shall see that even if the answer is yes then the problem of limits to care in allocating resources is vastly more complex than one which is open to any straightforward practical resolution. Some of the apparently practical problems in health care provision find their origin in other kinds of limits than mere shortfalls in resources. For example they have to do with conceptual limits connected with the enterprise of identifying and aggregating goods in health care provision. Such limits are centre stage in all maximisation theories of resource allocation in health care, the theoretical approach most favoured and that with which we shall be entirely concerned in this chapter. Beyond and beneath both these kinds of limits we can identify moral limits to the provision of health care which might impose either further restrictions on what may be offered to sufferers or, in other contexts, impose different patterns and methods of distribution on the resources allocated. Once such limits are recognised then we are faced with the problem of deciding who gets what, which calls should be heeded and which ignored. We shall also be pressed to give an account of who should make such decisions and on what basis.

159

## The problem of shortfalls

Is either side of the expression of the problem of the need for rationing in health care provision accurate? Is there really a shortage of resources? Is there really unlimited demand?

The two notions are of course in one sense inseparable. Unless there is unmet demand, or at least unmet need which may be quite a different matter, there cannot be a shortage of resources. Whether the resources thrown at a problem are adequate necessarily depends on the nature of the problem. If no health care needs remain unmet then it would be difficult to justify increased expenditure on the Health Service except in relation to correcting injustices of renumeration to health service employees or maintaining and improving hospital and other hardware provision in order to guarantee a continued adequate service. Though these additional issues do figure in discussions of the under-resourcing of the Health Service in the United Kingdom they are not the focus of the debate about rationing. It is the claim that the demands made on the service are unlimited which figures most prominently together with the obviously true claim that resources are not infinite. Even if the figure of 5.8% of the Gross National Product (GNP) spent on health care provision in the United Kingdom in 1991 (4.1% in 1950, 5.5% in 1976, 6.1% in 1983) (Appleby, 1992) was extended to the 14% of GNP spent on health care provision in the United States we would not guarantee that there would be no shortfall between resource and demand. Indeed the fact that there is such a glaring shortfall in the United States suggests the likelihood that the same would occur elsewhere - especially with the decline of automatic welfare state provision which is occurring in developed countries.

It would be false to imagine that the shortfall in the United Kingdom is a recent development. It has been convincingly argued that it is at least as old as the National Health Service itself (Drummond, 1980, p.2) - prior to which the provision of health care to large proportions of the population was admittedly inadequate, many of the population themselves not having the wherewithal to purchase the quality of health care which they required - a different version of the limited resources and unmet need equation. The ghost of inefficiency stalks the corridors of the National Health Service in the UK whose recent reforms suggest that the problem has been one of inefficient use of the resources available; though this has been strongly disputed, it being claimed contrarily that the quality and comprehensiveness of the health care purchased in the United Kingdom at around only 6% of GNP is remarkably good value for money (cf. Light, 1991). It rather looks like being the case that the shortfall between resource and demand or need is caused by the very success of the delivery of health care. Whereas the Beveridge Report believed that when the National Health Service was set up and resources were thrown

160

at the health problems of the nation those problems would be met, the health status of the population improve and the levels of demand decrease (cf. Culyer, 1976) no such outcome occurred. Though spending has increased the calls upon the Health Service have increased far more quickly. This should really surprise nobody, for a moment's reflection on just one health care intervention will illustrate the nature of the problem.

Consider the treatment of renal failure by dialysis. Only a couple of decades or so ago someone suffering renal failure would make immediate but brief demands on health care resources. Given the hopeless prognosis of the condition the terminal care of the patient would constitute the total demands that patient would make on the service. With the advent of renal dialysis, a medical success story, such lives can be saved and considerably extended even without the benefits of transplantation surgery. However, far from making a dent in the demands or needs knocking at the door of the health budget, so reducing costs, the very success of the therapy guarantees the production of an acute need for the rest of the patient's life - which may be many years. The cost of the dialysis fluids alone will commit the caring authorities to the expense of at least £10,000 per annum to which must be added the cost of maintaining surveillance and monitoring of the patient, dealing with infections and so on. The cost of success is therefore very high in that the meeting of one short term, albeit fundamentally acute, need creates a further acute long term need which commits considerable sums from the budget to a patient who, without treatment, would long since have made no demands whatsoever on health resources.

The same is true of many other areas of medical intervention. Indeed every life-saving intervention commits health authorities to the cost of continued care of the life saved. In the case of pre-term babies the initial heavy investment of resources guarantees a full lifetime of demands - in many cases of extraordinary demands. At the other end of life the success of the Health Service in improving the health status of the nation has resulted in very large numbers of people living very much longer than they would otherwise have done thus presenting the most serious drain of resources due to any group of patients. It is this level of efficient delivery of health care which has done the opposite to what the Beveridge Report expected. Each successful intervention, each new life-saving or life-enhancing technology has created new demands. Thus by its very nature health care provision is subject to unlimited demand - the more we have of it the more we shall expect and demand of it.

But given that a shortfall between resource and demand is inevitable in the nature of the case, how shall we make decisions about what ought or ought not to be provided, which demands ought or ought not to be met? Two approaches stand out as the main theoretical options. The first is the maximisation of benefit approach and the second, which may be a variant on

161

the first, the prioritising of need approach. Let us consider them in turn.


## The maximisation of benefit

This is by far the most popular approach recommended and practised in health care economics and is well expressed by the health economist Gavin Mooney as follows:

> What I would want to emphasise is that I see the issue here as being one of efficiency - essentially, maximising the benefit (however defined) to society at large from the resources available (however constrained). (Mooney, 1986, p.91)

This enterprise seems at first blush to be ethically unobjectionable or even admirable. In times of scarcity those resources used inefficiently on one patient are resources denied to another patient who stands in need of them - economists refer to this phenomenon in terms of opportunity costs. It is impossible to justify wasting valuable commodities. The only problem seems to be a practical one of determining what counts as the maximum benefit to be produced from a given unit of resource. If this was only a matter of complexity due to the intricate character of the calculations involved then resource allocation in health care would be no more than a tricky but morally non-threatening activity. However there is far more to it than appears. For a start it is blandly assumed in what has gone before that if maximum benefit is not achieved (given that such can be identified) then resources have been wasted. But is this obviously true? Something less than maximum benefit may nevertheless be morally worthwhile and justifiable. The saving of a life only to lose it within hours when the risks of such an outcome were high may signal the importance of other values than maximally efficient use of resources in our assessments of what is morally justifiable and what is not. Indeed, that resource allocation problems normally apply only at the margins of healthcare provision and not at its heart, for example in many acute interventions, denotes this.

But the problems with maximisation theories of resource allocation go deeper than this. They attach in part to conceptual limits to care, that is to limiting features of the concept of maximal benefit and of benefit *per se* and additionally to moral limits of care, that is to relations providers of care have towards individual sufferers and their respective perceptions of their suffering.

The theoretical stable of ethical theory out of which this model of resource allocation comes is that of consequentialism. It is exemplified in the utilitarianism of Jeremy Bentham and John Stuart Mill (cf. Mill, 1910) but is in fact a more general position of which there have been many variants produced even up until the present (see for example Griffin, 1986). The position holds that in order to determine what the right course of action is in any given situation one should attend only to the consequences of the action. In attending to these one should endeavour to calculate the greatest net balance of benefit over harm. Whichever action produces, or is likely to produce, the greatest good for the greatest number is the action which can be morally justified. It is clear that such a theoretical stance is attractive to planners of health care who have the responsibility, on behalf of the public, to best provide for the health needs of whole populations. Here attention to individual needs should, it would appear, not distort the overall allocation policy and, in the name of justice, each individual should count for one and no more than one (cf. Mill, p.58). There are traditional problems associated with such accounts of moral reflection which plague its application in the area of health care resource allocation. Much of what follows in this chapter is an effort to begin to identify and work out some of those difficulties.

## Cost-effectiveness analysis

Two of the major problems which traditionally threaten all consequentialist theories of ethics are the identification and the aggregation of goods. It will be interesting to enquire whether and to what degree these problems prove troublesome in the application of the two models of analysis employed in health economics which embody the maximisation principle as their *raison d'etre* - cost-effectiveness analysis and cost-benefit analysis. On the face of it the former, cost-effectiveness analysis, is the more ethically innocent of the two as it appears to avoid the problem of identification of goods *ex hypothesi* given that the good aimed for has to be written into the model before it can be applied. However the problem of aggregation of goods still arises in the application of the model, despite the apparently singular interest of the model in the selection of the good aimed for. In attending to this difficulty we might well discover that there is reason to doubt the absence of the problem of identification of goods in the model.

This tool of economic appraisal does not involve the setting of objectives or goals. It first demands that those planning health care provision present their chosen goals for analysis. The analyst then attends to the various means available to achieve those ends and endeavours to identify which are the most economical. Roughly speaking, if the goals can be maximised and the means minimised then maximal effectiveness will be achieved. However there almost always have to be trade-offs between these measures. Consider a hypothetical case. It may be that the application of a given screening regime for detecting genetic risk in potential parents would pick out 100 cases per 1000 screened if only families known to be at risk were entered into the programme. The cost per detected case would then be only 1 % of the budget allocated to the procedure. However by restricting the programme to known 'at risk' couples many other cases would necessarily go undetected. The programme could be extended in various ways. Maybe, for the sake of argument, there was some evidence of unequal demographic distribution of the conditions in question. It would then make sense to widen the pool of candidates for screening to include all potential parents in those areas under suspicion. The result would most likely be, even if there were special local causal agents present, that proportionally smaller numbers of cases would be detected in a greatly increased number of screenings. Let us imagine that they would amount to 10 further cases out of an extra 10,000 people screened. For each of this group of ten the costs would be, all other things being equal, 10% of a vastly greater budget. For each extension based upon more tenuous links between the selected groups and the condition to be detected the cost per detected case would increase at alarming rates. We would be faced with a situation of diminishing returns. It would become clear very quickly that vast sums of money would be required to detect each single extra case beyond a given point. The aim of maximising the goal would soon have to be abandoned because of its cost implications.

The balancing act between cost and outcome is even more demanding than this. It also involves the problems of aggregating goods despite the apparently singular good presented for analysis. Imagine a case where an apparently singular objective is set and cost-effectiveness analysis applied. For example, if by adopting a regime of day surgery fifty hernia operations can be performed for the cost of twenty by means of institutional care then, all other things being equal, this would be the most cost-effective and therefore the right form of management for which to opt, given that the maximal use of resources is the ideal goal for which to aim. The catch, even here, where like is being compared with like, is that all other things are rarely equal. It may be argued that all sorts of disagreements about what constitutes a successful outcome, what constitutes good care and so on might still arise. The emotional cost of anxiety caused to the patient by discharge to home so soon after surgery, the possibility of re-admission for complications, the burden on informal carers, possible prolongation in recovery time etc. cloud the issue. That a precise number of hernia surgeries were performed is but part of the story. These other considerations, the avoidance of which might go towards constituting a successful outcome, present additional objectives to be weighed against the set objective of performing the greater number of operations. Once this is recognised then cost-effectiveness analysis ceases to be useful, for all the objectives call for weighting and this is a task the analysis cannot perform. Yet it is one which always arises when the ethical dimension of outcomes is in question. Health economists recognise this limitation of cost-effectiveness analysis:

> Strictly, cost-effectiveness analysis can only cope with a programme in which there is a single output. This is because it cannot deal with different weights to be attached to multiple outputs. (Mooney, Russell and Weir, 1986, p.42)

So even in cost-effectiveness analysis both the problems of identifying goods and aggregating them occur, despite initial appearances. These problems are, however, explicit in cost-benefit analysis.


## Cost-benefit analysis

This economists' tool sets out to answer a different kind of question from the question of which means is the most effective to produce a given health care outcome. It endeavours rather to determine which health policies ought to be pursued by asking which outcomes are to be preferred in relation to the cost of achieving them. Before any calculation of the balance of goods can be attempted goods must first be identified and weighted. But this is by no means a straightforward matter as we have already begun to see. Not only are there problems in achieving universal agreement about what constitutes a good in the health care setting, there are additional problems in ranking those goods which are identified. For example, does the condition of sterility constitute a good or a harm? A little reflection will show that it is possible for people to disagree about this. For some people the inability to procreate is a blessing - indeed we have provided a facility in health care to achieve such a condition in both men and women by deliberately doing them a biological harm producing the condition which is a biological dysfunction. Though in some cases such procedures are designed to resolve or avoid other biological harms, in many cases the reason for the procedure is social or personal. Elsewhere in the health service we invest considerable sums of money to rectify such a dysfunction, or in some cases to circumvent it by means of assisted conception procedures. These are not available to large numbers of people because the purchasing authorities do not regard them as legitimate solutions to medical problems - or, in other words, do not regard the outcome of such procedures as health goods. How can cost-benefit analysis offer the planner any help here?

Many other examples could be cited. Perhaps the most dramatic cases are those where certain physiological conditions are recognised as calling for treatment in one place whereas they are thought to constitute no claim on treatment services in others. I have in mind here the condition of low blood pressure for which thousands of people are treated in Germany but for which no-one is treated in the United Kingdom. Or again cases where a given therapy may possibly be regarded by some patients as harmful by definition whatever the outcome for them. Think for example of procedures such as the control of diabetes by means of porcine insulin, the transfusing of blood, and the practice of so-called therapeutic abortion. We shall have more to say of such cases when we consider the identity of health needs as variously identified by the social context of the physiological conditions rather than by the biological facts themselves. The facts of benefit are socially constructed and are not simply givens about which there can be no dispute.

Yet cost-benefit analysis boldly claims to be able to help us in the area of identification of benefits whilst wearing its maximisation of benefits' heart on its sleeve.

> Ideally, if cost-benefit ananlysis were widely applied in health care, those policies that show the greatest benefit per £ of resources used should be given the greatest priority. Cost-benefit analysis thus has all the virtues and requirements of cost-effectiveness analysis plus the capacity to assist in decisions about worthwhileness. (Mooney, Russell and Weir, 1986, p.49)

How then can such a tool tackle the problems of identification and aggregation of benefits? It usually does so by producing a measure of benefit which can be universally applied to all health outcomes - that is, it assumes that all benefit is, in the last analysis, reducible to one kind of thing. This technique is a straight replication of that employed by John Stuart Mill in his utilitarian theory. For him all goods were cashable in terms of happiness. 'The utilitarian doctrine is, that happiness is desirable, and the only thing desirable, as an end; all other things being desirable as means to that end' (Mill, 1910, p.32).

Mill himself recognised problems with the employment of a single measure of what was regardable as a good and was eager to distinguish various kinds of happiness - some weighing far more than others - the higher pleasures, including intellectual pleasures, being more important or considerable than lower animal pleasures. Hence the dictum 'It is better to be a human being dissatisfied than a pig satisfied; better to be Socrates dissatisfied than a fool satisfied' (Mill, 1910, p.9). Arguments about both the identity and application of this measure have waged for many years without any consensus having been reached. One problem, for example, may be said to concern whether the measure involves what people do regard as happiness or rather what they ought to regard as happiness, for there are many who would quarrel with Mill's ordering of intellectual and animal pleasures. Mill leaves this task to a group of experts who are, in a sense, representing the view from nowhere in that they are simply picked out as suitable judges given their experiences of all the pleasures and pains in question. Furthermore they are to deal particularly with the tricky business of assessing the quality and quantity of goods:

> According to the Greatest Happiness Principle ... the ultimate end, with reference to and for the sake of which all other things are desirable (whether we are considering our own good or that of other people), is an existence exempt as far as possible from pain, and as rich as possible in enjoyments, both in point of quantity and quality; the test of quality, and the rule for measuring it against quantity, being the preference felt by those who in their opportunities of experience, to which must be added their habits of self-consciousness and self-observation, are best furnished with the means of comparison. (Mill, 1910, p.11)

Of particular interest in its application to resource allocation in health care he asks: 'What is there to decide whether a particular pleasure is worth purchasing at the cost of a particular pain, except the feelings and judgement of the experienced?' (Mill, 1910, p.10).

As he anticipates, in the health care setting we are immediately presented with precisely the same difficulties when devising and applying a singular measure of benefit. Who shall decide what that measure shall be based upon and whose weightings of various outcomes shall count in its creation? It is one thing to propose an abstract, unitary, theoretical measure which threatens no-one but the philosophically sensitive soul and quite another to produce an applied tool which must, to be applied at all, be invested with valuations of various outcomes. The moral attractiveness of the abstract measure - which as we have seen declares war on wasted resources - becomes morally threatening once it betrays a commitment to a particular set of valued outcomes.

Let us look at some examples to illustrate the point. The Welsh Office has produced a measure which it has called 'health gain' (Welsh Health Planning Forum, 1989). This is but one of a number of health status indices which have been produced by health economists. It is, like happiness, on the face of it a fine concept - what every health care intervention aims for is health gain for the patient. For practitioners to desire a deterioration in the health status of their patients would be as perverse and as counter-intuitive as someone's wanting to be unhappy. But, like happiness, health gain is an elusive entity to track down and measure.

Producing health gain is described as a two pronged activity - viz. adding years to life and adding life to years, precisely mirroring Mill's references to quantity and quality. In combining these elements it also resembles in many ways the QALY produced by Alan Williams who describes the measure as follows:

The essence of a QALY is that it takes a whole year of life expectancy to be worth 1, but regards a year of unhealthy life expectancy as worth less than 1. Its precise value is lower the worse the quality of life of the unhealthy person (which is what the 'quality adjusted bit' is all about). If being dead is worth zero, it is, in principle, possible for a QALY to be negative, i.e. for the quality of someone's life to be judged worse than being dead. (Williams, quoted in Harris, 1987, p.117)

Thus each of these indices is faced with the difficulties of identifying and measuring the added life produced by health care interventions. The quantity element of the measures is pretty crudely measured in terms of improvement in life expectancy and the mortality figures give some guide to us in this respect. However there is no consensus on what constitutes added quality in every respect nor how balances of added quality are to be calculated. For a start the kinds of goods to be weighed in the common balance of health gain, or QALYs, are simply incommensurable. We would each have difficulty ranking pains, immobility, healthy neonates, enhanced life expectancy, disfigurement, mental deterioration and so on as being more or less desirable than each other in our own experience. Presumably they would be ranked differently in different phases of our lives depending on our circumstances. Determining how much of one would be tradeable for how much of another is a further intellectual and emotional challenge. No doubt there would be very considerable ranges of disagreement between individuals if such ranking were attempted. How much more difficult it is when we pretend to be able to determine how one person's pain weighs against another's - how the moderate pain of one hundred sufferers weighs against the excruciating pain of one, or how the pain of one person is to be weighed against the immobility of another, and against the foreshortened life-expectancy of another, and against the safe delivery of another's child. We have then to add the challenge of the cases referred to earlier where conditions some regard as constituting health problems are not so identified by others.

Neither of the theoretical backgrounds of the indices mentioned put tools into our hands to determine these imponderables. The QALY theoreticians have employed an empirical model which seeks to determine a ranking by means of questioning a sample of the public as to their preferences. The sample was extremely small and unrepresentative. In any case such a method of fixing the measure would leave out the crucial question of whether conditions disvalued by minorities of people would thus be ruled out as possible candidates for health care interventions. We shall attend in more detail to this question of rival assessments of what are the important features of health status later when we consider the question of health care needs.

## The problem of justice

We have so far been concerned to examine two major problems with maximisation of benefit modes of health care resource allocation, viz. the identification and aggregation of goods. It would be mistaken to imagine that the ethical challenges faced by the maximisation of benefit are exhausted by these problems as we have so far examined them. Nevertheless we shall see that they continue to pose difficulties even when we face wider ethical challenges to the maximisation approach.

Consequentialism has numerous rivals in the field of ethical theory. Rights, duty and virtue theories immediately spring to mind. For example it has been well argued that gross injustices could result from pursuing a maximisation of benefit approach by using the QALY measure. The group inevitably discriminated against in the use of such a measure, it is claimed, is the aged. Where both quantity and quality of added life are incorporated into the measure of health outcome, those least likely to score well on the quantity side - those who are advanced in years and those who are suffering terminal illness - will be discriminated against. This may be said to constitute an inequity in access to treatment and be unfair, or it may be said to breach the rights such persons may have to access treatment services, for example by virtue of their lifelong payments to health insurance funds or by their low rate of demand on health services hitherto or both. Similarly those least likely to score well on the quality of life side of the equation - such as the terminally ill and the chronically sick - may be discriminated against as only marginal improvements in their condition can be achieved. Thus in addition to the burden of the debilitating condition they suffer they may face the further burden of losing the little improvement in health they could enjoy to others who, by means of the same resource enjoy the possibility of a far greater improvement in health. (John Harris (1987) has noted these two weaknesses in the application of the QALY measure.)

It is the issue of justice which is indeed the most prominent ethical challenge to maximisation theories. This should come as no surprise as it was the problem of justice which threatened to shipwreck John Stuart Mill's utilitarianism - indeed he recognised this himself though he was never able adequately to resolve the threat:

> In all ages of speculation, one of the strongest obstacles to the reception of the doctrine that Utility of Happiness is the criterion of right and wrong, has been drawn from the idea of justice. (Mill, 1910, p.38)

Those who follow in his footsteps often make the same acknowledgement. For example one leading health economist writes:

Whatever the financing mechanism, the question of justice and equity in health care seems important. Whatever else people dispute in health service policy, there is general agreement that fairness should be a part of health care. (Mooney, 1986, p.107)

Mooney goes on to show that preserving a place for efficiency whilst having regard for equity presents deep-going problems for health economists. One of the most obvious ways to attempt this is to measure efficiency of health care provision in terms of its success in meeting health care need as opposed simply to meeting health care demand. This will involve identifying and ranking needs to enable maximisation of benefit calculations to proceed again. However we then come up against our old problems of identification and aggregation of goods in another guise. To examine this claim let us consider an example of consequentialist resource allocation theory which makes justice or fairness a central consideration.[1]

**The prioritisation of need**

The theory, put forward by Daniels, effectively recasts what we have been considering as benefits, or aimed-for outcomes of health service provision, in terms of responses to negative states which constitute needs (Daniels, 1985). Thus, for example, the goal of amelioration of pain would be transposed into meeting a need for the relief of pain, increasing mobility would be transposed into meeting a need for relief of restriction of movement and so on. Thus we are enabled to introduce a rule of distributive justice into the scheme of maximisation. If we invest our resources in meeting needs then we will have ruled out the provision of unnecessary goods - non-essential demands. If, furthermore, we are committed to meeting the greatest need surely all will be well on the justice front. All that we shall now require is a criterion for identifying health needs which will also, if possible, be amenable to quantification. This will facilitate the ranking of outcomes and allow us to proceed with their aggregation, providing us with an equitable maximisation of benefit model. The proposed criterion is spelled out in terms of what Daniels labels the 'normal range of opportunity' (Daniels, 1985, pp.33-5). Health care needs impose limitations on how people are able to live their lives - they restrict the range of opportunity of those who suffer them. According to the degree in which a health care intervention restores a normal range of opportunity it ought, more or less, to be pursued.

Does this gesture towards fairness succeed in overcoming the major inadequacy of the maximising of benefit approach to health resource allocation? If it does, then it does so simply insofar as it gives us a possible

170

means of distinguishing needs from demands to which a bare maximisation of benefit theory would be indifferent. But much more than that it cannot offer us, because it runs into precisely the same problems in identifying health needs as we found earlier in identifying benefits. Further to this it also inherits the problems of incommensurability of needs, for now we have to determine not only whether a need of one kind is more pressing than a need of a very different kind but also how much of one need experienced by a large number of people outweighs how much of another in a smaller group of sufferers and so on. Moreover, despite appearances to the contrary, it too may be indifferent to degrees of need where they occur in certain groups or are of certain kinds. Let us briefly review this latter problem which presents itself in a slightly new form here from that indifference pointed out earlier in simple cost-benefit analysis cases.

Mill, in recognising that questions of ultimate ends were not amenable to direct proof, used the example of health as an illustration:

> Whatever can be proved to be good, must be so by being shown to be a means to something admitted to be good without proof. The medical art is proved to be good by its conducing to health; but how is it possible to prove that health is good? (Mill, 1910, p.4)

But we must ask whether what he claims to be true of health itself is not also true of particular health states. Because of the manner in which these individually inform the life of the person in question we may wish to consider them as goods in themselves. Daniels attends to this question in his treatment of health needs. He borrows a distinction to make his point, viz. that between course-of-life needs and adventitious needs (see Braybrooke, 1968, p.90). The former are needs which are basic to life whereas the latter are needs created by virtue of the adoption of various enterprises or ends. The former would be needs which men have *qua* men whereas the latter would be optional, in a sense. If, for example, I choose to build up body weight in order to compete as a heavyweight rather than a middleweight boxer then I will need additional supplies of red meat. However to survive at all I need food in the natural course of things.

Do all needs fall into such comfortable categories? The answer must be no for there are some features of a person's life without which their whole life will be rendered pointless which in another person's life may count for little. This may depend primarily on the social context of the condition or on the variety of social movements which pass through individuals in a pluralistic society, for example, the varying institutions of the family, religious perspectives, and so on.[2] Infertility is a prime example. It is not simply that someone needs to be fertile when they decide on the project of having children - though sometimes having a family may be no more than one project amongst others. For some women the inability to have children is a fundamental dysfunction which renders their whole life meaningless. That this might not be so with everyone or even a majority of people is beside the point. In the life in question it is regardable as a course-of-life need. It is the social setting of such features of life that determines which category they fall into (cf. Evans, 1996). Other examples could easily be cited such as longevity, physical grace, intelligence and even, in some cases, the amelioration of pain. Whilst not all societies would set great store on one or all of these, others would, and certainly individuals in various societies will vary in their assessment of the importance of them as features of a healthy life. Daniels himself acknowledges that the notion of normal opportunity range is too general to be straightforwardly applied because of limits placed upon it by such societal considerations, by age and other limiting factors (Daniels, 1985, p.33, pp.34-5, p.88). However he fails to see that his theory dies the death of a thousand qualifications as an attempt to find a common measure of human need.

## Conclusion

What then shall we say of maximisation theories of health resource allocation in conclusion? My quarrel is not with the attempt to eradicate wastage of scarce resources. Inefficiency is not a virtue. Indeed as a rule of thumb general maximisation techniques may offer us useful guides in planning health policies where there is a broad level of consensus on what constitutes health. However the application of such theories calls for modesty and sensitivity lest the interests of minorities be threatened and the preferences of self-appointed experts win the day in determining what health care provision people shall receive in ignorance of or in indifference to people's perceptions of their own lives and interests.

## Notes

1.  I have in mind the theory of Norman Daniels as set out in *Just Health Care* (1985). For a more detailed critique of this theory see Evans (1993).

2.  For a more detailed account of this phenomenon see Evans (1993).

# Bibliography

Appleby, J. (1992), *Financing Health Care in the 1990s*, Open University Press, Buckingham.

Braybrooke, D. (1968), 'Let needs diminish that preferences may prosper', in *Studies in Moral Philosophy*, American Philosophical Quarterly Monograph Series, No.1, Basil Blackwell, Oxford.

Culyer, A.J. (1976), *Needs and the National Health Service*, Martin Robertson and Co., London.

Daniels, N. (1985), *Just Health Care*, Cambridge University Press, Cambridge.

Drummond, M.F. (1980), *Principles of Economic Appraisal in Health Care*, Oxford University Press, Oxford.

Evans, D. (1993), 'Limits of care', in Evans, D. and Szawarski, Z. (eds), *Solidarity, Justice and Health Care Priorities*, Linkoping University, pp.28-41.

Evans, D. (1996), 'The clinical classification of infertility', in Evans, D. and Pickering, N. (eds) *Creating the Child*, Amsterdam, Martinuss Nijhoff, forthcoming.

Griffin, J. (1986), *Wellbeing: Its Meaning, Measurement and Moral Importance*, Clarendon Press, Oxford.

Harris, J. (1987), 'QALYfying the value of life', *Journal of Medical Ethics*, 13, pp.117-123.

Light, D.W. (1991), 'Observations on the NHS reforms: an American perspective', *British Medical Journal*, 303, pp.568-70.

Mill, J.S. (1910), 'Utilitarianism', in Rhys, E. (ed.), *Utilitarianism, Liberty, and Representative Government*, Everyman's Library, J.M.Dent and Sons Ltd., London, pp.1-60.

Mooney, G.H. (1986), *Economics, Medicine and Health Care*, Wheatsheaf Books Limited, Brighton.

Mooney, G.H., Russell, E.M. and Weir, R.D. (1986), *Choices for Health Care*, 2nd Edition, Macmillan, London.

Welsh Health Planning Forum (1989), *Strategic Intent and Direction for the NHS in Wales*, Welsh Office, Cardiff.

Welsh Health Planning Forum (1989), *Strategies for Health: A New Approach to Local Strategic Planning*, Welsh Office, Cardiff.

# 11 Ethical review of medical research and health policy

*Rupert Jarvis*

## Introduction

> Live cancer cells were injected into 22 human subjects as part of a study of immunity to cancer ... the subjects (hospitalized patients) were 'merely told they would be receiving "some cells"' - 'the word cancer was entirely omitted'. (Beecher, 1966, p.1358)

In 1994 in the UK, if you were a woman seeking assisted conception services, and you were not in a stable heterosexual relationship, then fifteen health authorities would have refused to fund your treatment. If you had challenged their decision, they would have told you that demand for assisted conception services enormously outstripped supply, that the authority could not afford to purchase all the treatment cycles that were wanted, that money was very tight, and that there were other areas of the health service where the money was needed more.

What have these two examples to do with each other? One deals with medical research, with pushing back the frontiers of knowledge and practice, while the other is about rationing treatment, about deciding who shall get and who shall go without. Surely the clinical concerns are for clinicians to guard against, and managers are paid to balance the books, and decisions about where to direct the money are for them to worry about. Is there anything more to say?

I believe that there is a great deal more to say about both these issues.[1] Moreover, I suggest that the two areas, of medical research and of health policy, are considerably more closely related than may at first appear. I shall argue that the two are linked in respect of the kinds of moral difficulties to which they give rise, and I shall sketch some attempts in both fields to address these concerns. However, although I believe that there are related moral concerns that run through both medical research and health policy, nonetheless it is clear that there are substantial areas where the two do not overlap. I shall therefore treat them separately to begin with, before moving to consider what it is that they have in common.

## The individual as the end point of suffering

Before we move to consider features specific to either medical research or health policy, let us be clear that all activity within the field of health care takes place within an inescapably *moral* framework. What I mean by that goes well beyond the traditional approach of medical ethics narrowly construed, that contented itself with spotting *specific* areas of practice (embryology, care of the dying, genetic manipulation, and so on). The traditional picture of the relationship between medicine and morality to which this approach gave rise suggested that the two realms were distinct, with tangential points at which they overlapped.[2]

We can think of the traditional picture as depicting morality[3] as being in parallel with all the other aspects of good medical practice, as if it were another layer added to the ever growing pile. The schema that I am suggesting, by contrast, holds that morality runs *through* the whole of health care provision at all levels. It is not so much another layer as a vertical line that cuts through existing divisions in practice and institutions. To use a biblical analogy, it is like the yeast in the bread, that permeates all aspects of service planning and delivery. The inescapable fact of health care provision is that it necessarily involves, at all levels, a complex interplay of human costs, benefits and harms. Lest we forget, people hurt and die in hospitals.

I suggest that it is impossible to imagine any area of health care not in some way tinged with this inescapably moral flavour: that there is, to put it another way, an irreducibly moral dimension to health care research and planning at all levels. More specifically to our present purposes, we can see immediately that in the case of both medical research and of health policy decision making, the end-point of suffering is located firmly within the individual: that is, real people are affected by the decisions taken. At his moment of tragic self recognition towards the end of Miller's play, Keller says of the young airmen killed as a result of his carelessness 'I think ... they were all my sons ... I guess they were' (Miller, 1961, p.170): his acknowledgement of the inescapably moral quality of his actions is one from which much analysis of health care could profitably learn.

This necessary feature of health care delivery, that it is *people* who are affected by it, assumes an even greater importance when we consider that those whom the current market jargon refers to as the consumers of health

176

care, people who might formerly have been called research subjects or patients, are inevitably *vulnerable*. I argued (Jarvis, 1995) that the power differential implicit in a consultation between professional and layperson, particularly when that latter is 'upset, powerless, frightened, and not feeling at all well' (Whitehorn, 1993, p.110), means that every health care encounter involves a vulnerable party, the consumer. This holds equally true whether we consider the case of research or of normal practice: in either case, an individual is clearly at risk. It is this risk that places those involved in any way in health care delivery under an obligation to ensure the review of research and practice.

The task of such review must be to ensure that the risk to the individual is, if not eliminated, at least proportional to the intended benefits. In research, as in all areas of health care activity, professionals deal with the vulnerable, the worried, and the sick. In the context of health policy decision making, tragic choices have to be taken that will mean that some individuals will be denied access to health care. The over-riding question in the latter case is a stark one: 'Who will live, in what degree of pain and discomfort, when all must ultimately die?' (Sheldon and Maynard, 1993, p.4).

Before going on to look at the specific processes involved in the ethical review of medical research and health policy, I want to suggest another area of similarity between the two fields, in terms of the relative importance accorded to the interests of the individual and of society.

It is a familiar theme in any scheme of ethics derived from the thought of Immanuel Kant that we owe a moral obligation to others to treat them as ends in themselves, and not simply as means to an end of our own (see O'Neill, 1991). Of course, I may treat someone as a means to my end: my interactions with the cobbler at the end of my road are confined almost entirely to getting my heels on my shoes replaced. But if the occasion arose, that is, if the moral flavour that permeates all our lives came to the surface - if, for instance, in replacing a heel he rapped his thumb with his hammer - then some sort of moral response, sympathy, at the very least, and perhaps a bandage, is demanded of me. I should not, that is, think of the cobbler as a means of getting my shoes fixed *simpliciter*: as a fellow human being, he demands more of me than that I treat him *only* as an means, in the way that I might treat an inanimate object. Even radical capitalists are compelled to acknowledge that there is a moral difference between a tool and the worker who operates it.

I suggest that the dangers of exploitation of individuals as means to an end not chosen by themselves are writ particularly large in the fields of medical research and health policy. Part of the danger springs from the impersonal, anonymising effect of large scale institutions and endeavours: from losing sight of the fact noted above, that the end-point of suffering is located within the individual. To understand all may not in this case be to forgive all, but it

177

is perhaps possible to understand how the directors of a large scale research effort simply lose sight of the fact that there are real people out there taking unproven drugs, or having their artificial hips fitted with trial cement, or whatever the focus of the research might be: somebody's father, somebody's son. Large scale clinical research may appear to deal in columns of figures, but what is too easily forgotten is that every figure in those tables has pains, hopes, and fears of their own. They, no less than the researchers, are people.

In the same way, it has often been noted that it is easy, too easy, for health service managers, sitting behind a desk, to forget that genuinely ill, worried people are affected every day by the decisions they take. It is often suggested that health service managers operate in comfortable isolation from the 'real world' of medicine with its suffering and fear. These pictures are often overdrawn to the point of caricature, but we should at least acknowledge the danger, in management just as in research, of losing sight of the individual.

## Costs and benefits

We can see, then, that while the apparent currency of both research and health policy is the nameless cypher, in fact conclusions, decisions and practice at these levels have a direct and very real effect on actual people. This leads us to a significant similarity between the two fields, that both run the risk of sacrificing the present interests of individuals in order to secure or promote those of the wider society (or in the case of research, of future societies). Clinical research, by the time it has reached the stage of trials in human subjects, is about testing procedures, therapies or drugs in order to see whether or not they will be of benefit. That is, research (at least runs the risk of) sacrificing the interests of present individuals in order to secure potential benefits in the future. Similarly, health policy decisions involving questions about allocating scarce resources involve denying treatment to one in order to make it available to another; again, playing off the interests of one individual against others.

It is perhaps in view of this danger that the World Medical Council's Declaration of Helsinki lays down that: 'In research on man, the interest of science and society should never take precedence over considerations related to the wellbeing of the subject' (reprinted in Mason and McCall Smith, 1991, p.446-9). In Kantian terms, we might say that there is a duty on researchers to treat their subjects as ends in themselves, and not simply as means to an end of their own. However, as Goodare and Smith (1995, p.1277) noted, 'clinical trials cannot be done without patients'. The indispensability of the patient (or the volunteer) to the conduct of a clinical trial sets up a tension between the interests of that individual and those of society, science or the

178

researcher. It is, *inter alia*, this tension that should be addressed by ethical review.

We should be clear that the alternatives to conducting clinical research or engaging in deliberative policy decisions carry a heavy opportunity cost. The choice, roughly speaking, is between a planned development of practice and provision on the one hand, and an *ad hoc*, piecemeal approach on the other. There is a self-evident public interest in good clinical research taking place, and it is widely accepted that rationing is inevitable in health care provision.[4] If research is desirable and rationing inevitable, it is reasonable to suggest that, given the possibilities for harm to individuals, they should be reviewed rather than not. Ethical review of clinical research is a relatively well established idea in the UK; the first Research Ethics Committees (RECs) were established in the 1960s. Review of commissioning, rationing and health policy decisions is a newer development, which owes something to the relative transparency of the decision making process following the 1991 reforms of the NHS that lead one commentator to remark that: 'fifty years of muddling through elegantly [in treatment rationing decisions] are now definitely at an end' (*HSJ* editorial, 1995, p.17).

## Reviewing research: aims and purpose

So what does the process of ethical review of clinical research involve, and what problems does it aim to address? Certainly, the scope of the review is broad: an REC must be consulted where a project involves NHS patients, foetal material and *in vitro* fertilisation involving NHS patients, the recently dead on NHS premises, access to records, and use of NHS facilities or premises (DoH, 1991). We might say that RECs have a right to review all NHS related research.

However, the sheer scale of this right creates its own problems. Most members of RECs are busy professionals, and their time - given voluntarily - is limited. As the number of protocols being presented to RECs increases, the supposed right to review is in danger of boiling over into a painful duty, as the review load rises apparently inexorably. The danger implicit in this is that RECs will not have time to review each protocol as fully as they would wish. This may result either in protocols being approved that should perhaps have been referred from representation, or in research that might eventually have been approved by the REC being rejected in haste.

The vast majority of protocols seen by RECs involve so-called Phase III trials, where 'early safety testing has already been done and a study on a reasonably large scale, usually conducted on a multi-centre basis, is a requirement in order to obtain a product licence from the Medicines Control

Agency' (Neuberger, 1992, p.10). These trials may relate to epidemiological data, surgical procedures, or behavioural research, among other possibilities, but considerably the largest proportion involves drug trials sponsored by the pharmaceutical industry. Of these trials, most are randomised control trials (RCTs), where patients and volunteers on the trial are divided into two arms, one of which receives the new drug, and the other a placebo. Neither the patients, nor the researchers, nor the patients' doctors, know which trial arm any one individual is on;[5] this procedure is designed to eliminate fraudulent or biased results.

So much for the scope and arena of the RECs' review. We now turn to the question of what problems they seek to address. To put this question another way, what are they looking for that could go wrong?

The first thing to note is that the RECs can be seen (and see themselves, see Neuberger, 1992, p.44) as public watchdogs, as checking, on behalf of the public - on whom and in whose name the research is being carried out - that the proposal meets certain standards. The underlying image is that members of the public are prevented from doing this on their own behalf either because they lack access to important information about the research, or because they do not know that it is happening in the first place. The RECs, then, can be seen as acting on behalf of the public, ensuring that the interests of individual members of the public are not subsumed in a glib 'public interest' argument.

As a starting point, the RECs examine the proposed research for scientific validity, on the grounds that research of poor quality cannot be justified. They then move to the more difficult ethical evaluation of the protocol. Although the proposals are reviewed with reference to a number of questions, two stand out as absolutely central to the process: the question of consent, and the weighing of risks and benefits.

The number of difficulties clustering around the issue of consent is vast, but they can be roughly grouped under two heads: whether the consent is truly voluntary, and whether it is properly informed. There is a vast body of literature on the subject (Faulder, 1987, provides a good overview), and we cannot address it properly here. We should, however, note that research on certain groups is particularly prone to expose lay individuals in those groups to improper coercion or pressure: that is, to call into question or even to invalidate their consent. Such groups include children, the very old and the mentally ill, where there may be doubts about the level of information, as well as the students and subordinates of the researcher, the financially disadvantaged, or those in long term institutional care, where one might question the voluntariness of the consent.

In all these groups, there is room for particular concern that the consent obtained may either not be adequately informed or not properly voluntary. There are no clear answers to the questions clustering around the issue of consent, and the problems that it raises remain central to the work of any ethical review of clinical research. At all times, there remains the tension that we identified above, between the interests of the individual and the interests of society, between the imperative to research and the individual's reluctance to participate in such research, and it is the goal of the REC to ensure that this tension is not improperly resolved.

The weighing of risks and benefits is no easier to undertake, and no more susceptible to easy answers. Indeed, it has been argued that moral dilemmas are such that their very nature is that they are not the sort of questions that can be answered simply (see Jarvis, 1995). Article I, 4 of the Declaration of Helsinki lays down that: 'biomedical research involving human subjects cannot legitimately be carried out unless the importance of the objective is in proportion to the inherent risk to the subject' (reprinted in Mason and McCall Smith, 1991, pp.446-9).

Although this principle looks straightforward, its application is anything but. Firstly, there is no reason to suppose that there will be just one objective of the trial: typically, in the case of a phase III trial, the purpose is in part to further human knowledge, and to extend the boundaries of clinical practice in the interests of future patients, but it is often in part to gain a product licence to ensure a competitive market share (in research sponsored by pharmaceutical companies), or to gain academic or personal prestige (in research presented by individuals or smaller teams). This is not necessarily to denigrate such protocols, but it is to suggest that research objectives are, as Wilde put it, 'rarely pure and never simple' (Wilde, 1966).

The second thing to note from the above excerpt from the Helsinki Declaration is that risk is seen as being inherent in research. As Neuberger (1992, p.44) argues:

All research involving human subjects carries with it the risk that the subjects will be unaware of the full importance of what they are being asked to do, and that they will sometimes be asked to enter research studies which are poorly designed, carry some material risk, or could in some way cause emotional or physical distress.

The suggestion that no research can take place on human subjects without risk links with our earlier argument that there is no field of health care activity that is free from moral concern: health care in all its forms, whether research or practice, is irredeemably bound up with goods and harms, benefits and risks; and where there is this potential, there is moral concern.

## Reviewing health policy

*The problem*

Moral considerations are similarly inescapable in the field of health policy. Whether we talk of priority setting, or of targeted investment, or of rationing, there is an increasing acceptance in the NHS that: 'choices have ... to be made about the use of available funds and priorities have to be set' (Royal Commission on the NHS, 1979, p.51). This acceptance is, however, by no means universal.[6] It will therefore pay us to examine this question of the elasticity of demand for health care and to discuss its implications for health policy and provision.[7]

The foundation of the NHS was marked by a mood of optimism and - arguably blind - confidence: 'one of the assumptions made in the Beveridge Report was that expenditure on health services would decline once the backlog of ill health which was thought to exist in the community had been eradicated' (Ham, 1992, p.38). Sadly, this assumption was then - and remains now - utterly mistaken.

It is mistaken for conceptual reasons. That is to say, its mistake will remain a mistake even if the purely practical reasons for the NHS's underfunding were eliminated. Even if it were not the case that demographic changes since 1948 meant that the proportion of the population over 65 (where health spending is highest) had almost doubled, leading to a scenario of rising health care costs and proportionally fewer producers of taxation revenue, and even if the basis on which public spending is allocated were cataclysmically altered tomorrow, say by abandoning all defence and security spending and rerouting the released revenue into the NHS, there would still not be enough to go around, except perhaps in the immediate short term. These practical problems of demographic change and politically generated underfunding may exacerbate the problem of shortfall, but they do not cause it. The cause lies in the very concept of health itself.

Lefeber (1990, p.75) argues that it is a lack of clarity about this concept that has generated most of the NHS's problems, and Smith (1993, p.ix) takes up this theme, suggesting that: 'no health care system will be stable unless it answers the question of what is covered'.

Time, perhaps then, for some clarity about the nature of the concept of health, and why demand for health care is potentially infinite. Firstly, the increasingly effective health care that the NHS delivers carries its own implied burden of rising demand: as people are enabled to live longer as a result of successful health care interventions, so both the number of years for which they continue to draw on health care resources, and the quantum of that draw increase. As Mason and McCall Smith (1991, p.272) argue: 'every sudden death in late middle age that is prevented is potentially a long-term occupancy of a bed in a psychogeriatric ward ...'. Secondly, as Lefeber suggests, the fact that there is no clear or static boundary around the notion of health means that there are no limits to what can be demanded in the name of health care.[8]

*Attempted solutions*

Rationing is therefore an inescapable part of health care provision for both practical and logical reasons. Far from reducing a fixed need, increased activity actually creates new demand, as the Norwegian experience shows:

The result of all these efforts [to eliminate waiting lists] was not that fewer people ended up on waiting lists, but that many more patients were treated than before. Again, supply seems to have created demand ... many believed, mistakenly, that each waiting list reflected the real distance between objective need and real capacity, and that problems ... could be solved by channelling more money into hospitals to wipe out waiting lists. They were surprised that the waiting lists did not decrease as a result of the extra funding. (Government Committee on Choices in Health Care, 1992, p.100)

Given this necessary elasticity of demand and perceived need, it should be clear that any attempt to duck the inevitability of rationing is doomed to failure. Attempts to make the NHS more efficient by introducing and strengthening general management (in 1974, 1982 and 1984), or by deploying 'the unseen hand of the market' to bring down costs through competition (in 1991) may have been useful attempts to push back the point at which the need to ration treatment bit, in that they may have allowed more to be squeezed out of the same lemon, but they could not - logically could not - have eliminated the need to ration.[9] In the same way that previous reforms had aimed to address the problem of incomplete health care coverage by introducing management systems to direct resources more effectively, the 1991 shake up put its faith in competition to ensure that the health care delivery was maximally efficient. What no reforms could escape was the logical point that we discussed earlier: that no health care activity saves money - it necessarily generates further demand for existing resources, what Evans (1994) calls the 'legacy of need' of successful delivery.

This inevitability of rationing has been more widely accepted than acted upon: the Royal Commission's Report quoted above identified its inescapability in 1979, and yet 12 years later, the service was still being reformed with an eye to eliminating waste and so doing away with the need to deny treatment at all. However, one effect of the 1991 reforms, as we noted above, has been the increasing transparency of rationing decisions and, in part, the mechanisms by which they are taken. Certainly, it would be idle now to pretend that rationing is not an everyday part of health policy and management at all levels, from the GP deciding how short she can cut the next consultation in order to get to the clinic on time, to the Senior Executive Team of a Health Authority deciding how many cycles of IVF to purchase in the next financial year.

This growing realisation that the problems posed by rationing are not simply going to vanish in the face of new efficiency savings, coupled with the knowledge that decisions are now taken in a media spotlight, has prompted various attempts to come to terms with the problems of health policy: what we might call the beginnings of an ethical review of health policy.

In Oregon, a now notorious round of public consultation sought to list several hundred condition/treatment pairs in order of democratically accorded priority, with a view to disinvesting in all those that fell below a critical line.[10] Doubts have been raised about the value of the exercise that centred partly on the level of information that grounded the public consultation, and partly on the revelation that health care experts 'adjusted' the results in order to smooth out some of the more (to them) counter-intuitive solutions. Quite aside from these difficulties, there is a danger in ruling out entire treatments or conditions that the model thus created may prove inflexible and unable to respond to the clinical need of an individual. While it may be true that much cosmetic surgery is what we might call 'vanity work', we can imagine cases where there may be a genuine need for the treatment that could not be met if cosmetic surgery *per se* were proscribed: ruling out whole areas of treatment or entire conditions as proposed in Oregon leaves clinicians unable to formulate a proper moral response to identified suffering.

In New Zealand, a more evolutionary approach was proposed, that suggested that a core of services that had grown up since the inception of the health service be maintained in the public sector with individuals electing to take out private cover for other services. Although this suggestion is attractive in that it urges a developmental model rather than the wide excision approach of Oregon, it gives rise to the immediate and so far intractable problem of defining the boundaries of the service core.

A similar definitional problem was encountered in Holland, where a model of four filters was proposed, whereby only treatments and therapies that measured up to all four criteria would be funded out of the public purse. The model would have ruled out any treatment that was considered not necessary, or ineffective, or inefficient, or to fall within the remit of individual responsibility. However, the inherently subjective and open textured nature of the definitions meant that it was far from clear which (if any) treatments should be funded according to this model.

The British tradition of rationing has been characterised (Ruddle, 1991) as rationing by deterrence and delay: responses to the tension of limited supply and infinite demand have tended to attempt to divert demand, especially to the private sector, or to rely on waiting lists as a - somewhat heavy handed - tool to manage demand. Neither approach is particularly satisfactory, and this has become more obvious since the 1991 reforms. It was with regard to this problem, and the absence of any guidance or mechanisms for ensuring the fairness of rationing, that one Health Authority, West Glamorgan, established an experimental purchasing ethics committee in 1992.[11]

The committee's task was to provide ethical review and advice relating to dilemmas in health policy. It can therefore be seen as a deliberate attempt to face up to and grapple with the newly public difficulties faced by health care rationers at all levels. Although in one sense this represents a new direction for health policy in Britain, in another it can be seen as a very modest development. There has been, for instance, no attempt on the part of the committee to give the impression of handing out wisdom from on high: that is, the simplistic model of some attempts at ethical analysis (see for instance Seedhouse, 1988) that purport to act as ethical algorithms has been explicitly rejected. The recommendations instead appear to endorse the conclusion that 'given the complexity of the question[s] under consideration, we should not be in the least bit surprised that [they are] susceptible to no solution entirely free of moral cost' (Jarvis, 1995).

It may be asked of any experiment of this nature 'Has it worked? Has anything changed, or do things carry on much as ever they did?'. In attempting to measure the effectiveness of an initiative such as the West Glamorgan purchasing ethics committee, there is a danger in looking too closely for the dramatic *volte face*, the sudden reversal of policy, and neglecting the value of the more gradual change. Like the New Zealand approach that stressed the importance of an evolutionary perspective, and suggested that a value should be accorded to those services that had withstood the passage of time, the West Glamorgan experiment should be seen as attempting to effect a gradual change. Its concern was not to head off particular policies, but to draw out the foundational philosophy and value sets that grounded institutional policy decisions. The aim was to change the process of decision making, not to alter specific decisions: by a trickle down effect, to bring about a change in the climate of decision making.

## Comparing reviews: learning the lessons

So what merit is there in considering ethical review of clinical research and of health policy under one head? What comparisons can we bring out, and what can each learn from the other?

Review of research is notable for the minute detail in which proposals are examined, almost as if there was a concern that some fine point of interest may be hidden away beneath the glossy veneer of pharmaceutical corporate respectability. To an extent, there may be a grain of truth in this worry, in that there is certainly a danger of being wooed by the slick presentation and apparent professionalism of international drug company protocols. We can be certain, too, that it is easy to slide into valuing clinical research for its own sake, rather than for the sake of any benefits that it might bring to research subjects or future patients.

However, there is a well known myopia associated with woods and trees, and the current model of ethical review of research might do well to reflect on the general principles that ground it, as well as the details of particular research proposals. It is these very general principles that Michels and Rothman (1994, p.397) refer to when they argue that 'above all, scientific imperatives should never be weighed against established ethical ones'. Chief among the ethical principles that they cite is 'the precept that patients ought not to face unnecessary pain or disease on account of a medical experiment' (1994, p.397).

By contrast, early attempts at ethical review of health policy have tended, as we noted above, to concentrate more on seeking to effect a change in the climate of decision making, rather than to pursue particular decisions. With the possible exception of the Oregon experiment, most attempts in this area have sought to clarify what it is that underpins the provision of health care services: by reflection and analysis, it is hoped that a clearer conception will emerge.

However, we must beware of too readily accepting a stark dichotomy when the reality is less clear cut. While RECs tend in general to concentrate on details, and policy review looks more at the broader picture, this sketch is - and should be - more blurred than sharp. I have already suggested that there may be a place for including broader considerations in the review of research, and certainly review of policy cannot be properly undertaken without clear reference to the detailed facts of the situation of investment: at the very least, there is an immediate need for wide ranging research to determine the effectiveness of much of what is presently taken as standard practice.[12]

Linked to this conception of research review as detailed and policy review as broader in scale is a similar, although this time rather starker, distinction. RECs, by the nature of their constitution and working patterns, operate as 'advisory bod[ies], examining only the material with which [they are] confronted' (Neuberger, 1992, p.44). Ethical review of health policy, however, has tended to be more pro-active, in that attempts have been made to begin the process quite apart from any specific rationing or other policy decisions. Highlighted cases, such as the Child B case referred to above, serve to give a new impetus and temporary focus to the debate, but in general policy review has tended to set its own agenda, rather than being restricted to considering questions presented to it by concerned professionals.

While there may be differences - perhaps of degree rather than of kind - between the two forms of ethical review that we have considered, there remains one fundamental similarity between the two enterprises. It is a fitting place to end this discussion, as it reflects the central importance of philosophy in health care activity at all levels, from the most specific to the extremely generalised. Modern health care, too often in the grip of a technological imperative, loses sight of the paramount importance of the individual as its chief end and sole locus of suffering at the peril both of the individual and of health care practice. The primary concern of ethical review of health care practice at any level should be to ensure that the vulnerable individual is adequately protected. As members of a moral community, it is to one another that we owe our moral allegiance and duties, and nowhere are these duties more clearly expressed than in our relations with those more dependent than ourselves.

The grounding belief of both forms of ethical review is that vulnerable individuals can best be protected by requiring a clarity of process in all areas. By exposing the risk analyses and value bases on which a proposal rests, we who stand to benefit from or be harmed by the proposal can give or withhold our consent. This belief in the value of philosophical enquiry in exposing, questioning and clarifying that which remains hidden and unexamined illustrates two foundational principles of the discipline: the Socratic doctrine, that the unexamined life is not worth living, and Parker's (1994, p.35) contention that philosophical 'argumentation is an inherently democratic model of influence ... involving ... a commitment to the canons of clear argument and open debate', and represents a rediscovery of the original values and objectives of philosophical enquiry.

## Notes

1.  Readers interested in exploring further abuses of research would do well to consult Lifton (1986). Freemantle (1993) and Freemantle et al. (1993) give interesting examples of curious, or worse, decisions taken by health purchasers in the UK.

2. This picture is echoed in the 'bolt-on' approach to the introduction of medical ethics into the undergraduate medical curriculum, as if ethics were nothing more than yet another area of potential specialisation.

3. Or ethics, if you prefer. For the purpose of this chapter, I shall make no distinction between the terms.

4. This view is not universally accepted (see Roberts et al., 1995), and I argue for it below.

5. Although there is a code that can be broken in the event of a clinical emergency.

6. See for instance Roberts et al., 1995.

7. Even after ethical review of rationing decisions, there still remain substantive moral questions about the way in which a set amount of resources once allocated is deployed. Present interest in the NHS, however, is concentrated very much on the issue of rationing and differential commissioning of services.

8. The debates and periodic redefinitions that take place at the margins of health care, such as disputes over whether infertility represents a *health* need (as opposed to a social need or preference), or whether gender realignment therapy is part of the properly construed canon of health care, emphasise the importance of such questions. It is also significant that questions such as 'Is infertility really a health need?' are most commonly found in the context of health policy decisions.

9. Indeed, the highly publicised 'Child B' case in Cambridgeshire, where the Health Authority decided not to purchase a second bone marrow transplant for a 10 year old girl with leukaemia, gives weight to the suggestion that the effect of the 1991 reforms has been not to eliminate rationing decisions but simply to bring them out into the open. White (1995, p.20) quotes a politician as saying that 'the NHS has always had to make judgements of this kind, but it has not had to make them on TV'.

10. Strosberg, 1992, provides a useful overview of the process.

11. In the wake of the child B case, a further development has been proposed, with Cambridge and Huntingdon Health Authority suggesting that they might establish a Citizens' Jury, selected at random from the

electoral roll, to review individual case management decisions. At the time of writing, however, this remains a theoretical initiative.

12. York and Leeds Universities' *Effective Health Care Bulletins*, and *The Bandolier* published by Anglia and Oxford Regional Health Authority are useful initiatives in the move towards evidence based health policy. There are also on-line discussion groups available for Internet users, reflecting a growing awareness of the need for evidence based health care in all areas. See also Appleby et al., 1995.

**Bibliography**


Appleby, J., Walshe, K., Ham, C. (1995), *Acting on the Evidence: A Review of Clinical Effectiveness, Sources of Information, Dissemination and Implementation*, National Association of Health Authorities and Trusts, Birmingham.
Beecher, H. (1966), 'Ethics and clinical research', *New England Journal of Medicine*, Vol. 274, No. 24, pp.1354-60.
Department of Health (1991), *Local Research Ethics Committees*, HSG(91)5, August.
Evans, D. (1994), 'A health care planner's conscience', *Cambridge Quarterly of Healthcare Ethics*, Vol. 3, pp.108-15.
Faulder, C. (1987), *Whose Body Is It? The Troubling Issue of Informed Consent*, Virago, London.
Freemantle, N. (1993), 'Rationing infertility services', (editorial), *The Lancet*, Vol. 342, pp.251-2.
Freemantle, N., Watt, I. and Mason, J. (1993), 'Developments in the purchasing process of the NHS: towards an explicit politics of rationing', *Public Administration*, Vol. 71, pp.535-48.
Goodare, H. and Smith, R. (1995), 'The rights of patients in research: patients must come first in research', *British Medical Journal*, Vol. 310, pp.1277-8.
Government Committee on Choices in Health Care (1992), *Choices in Health Care (The Dunning Report)*, Ministry of Welfare, Health and Cultural Affairs, Rijswijk.
Ham, C. (1992), *Health Policy in Britain: The Politics and Organisation of the National Health Service*, 3rd edition, Macmillan, Basingstoke.
*HSJ* editorial (1995), 'Rationing needs a rational policy', *Health Service Journal*, 16 March.
Jarvis, R. (1995), 'A potential tragedy in six acts? Ethical dilemmas in electronic patient register research', forthcoming in *Health Informatics*.

Lefeber, R. (1990), 'Decision making', in Devlin, B. et al. (eds) (1990), *Medical Care: is it a consumer good?* IFEA Health and Social Welfare Unit, London.

Lifton, R. (1986), *The Nazi Doctors: Medical Killing and the Psychology of Genocide*, Basic Books, New York.

Mason, J. and McCall Smith, R. (1991), *Law and Medical Ethics*, Butterworths, London.

Michels, K. and Rothman, K. (1994), 'The continuing unethical use of placebo controls', *New England Journal of Medicine*, Vol. 331, pp.394-8.

Miller, A. (1961), *All My Sons*, Penguin, Harmondsworth.

Neuberger, J. (1992), *Ethics and Health Care: The Role of Research Ethics Committees in the United Kingdom*, King's Fund Institute, London.

O'Neill, O. (1991), 'Kantian ethics', in Singer, P. (ed.), *A Companion to Ethics*, Basil Blackwell, Oxford.

Parker, J. (1994), 'Moral philosophy - another 'disabling profession'?', in Chadwick, R. (ed.), *Ethics and the Professions*, Avebury, London.

Ruddle, S. (1991), *Rationing Resources in the NHS*, Institute for Health Policy Studies, University of Southampton, Southampton.

Roberts, C. et al. (1995), 'Rationing is a desperate measure', *Health Service Journal*, January, p.15.

Royal Commission on the National Health Service (1979), *Report*, Cmnd 7615, HMSO, London.

Seedhouse, D. (1988), *Ethics: The Heart of Health Care*, John Wiley and Sons, Chichester.

Sheldon, T. and Maynard, A. (1993), 'Is rationing inevitable?', in Smith (ed.) (1993).

Smith, R. (ed.) (1993), *Rationing in Action*, BMJ Publishing Group, London.

Strosberg, M. (ed.) (1992), *Rationing America's Medical Care: The Oregon Plan and Beyond*, Brookings Institute, Washington.

White, M. (1995), 'Life is unfair, even to kids', *Health Service Journal*, 16 March, p.20.

Whitehorn, K. (1993), 'Surely you're not going to ration *me!*', in Smith (ed.) (1993).

Wilde, O. (1966), *The Importance of Being Earnest*, Eyre Methuen, London.

# 12 Third world aid: Boundaries and responsibilities

*Richard Bryden*

## The problem

Health care in the developed world (the so-called first world) is dominated by concern about the diseases of affluence and the problems associated with ageing populations and with high-tech medicine. By contrast, debates about third world health care are dominated by the diseases of malnutrition, social dislocation and extreme poverty, and by problems associated with high infant and child mortality and a low life expectancy. These problems have two unmistakeable features: first, the huge absolute amount of urgent unmet need and second its worrying persistence.

The suffering which this unmet need entails is overwhelmingly attributable in the first instance to public health issues such as polluted water supplies, and to unfit or overcrowded living accommodation both in rural areas and in the mushrooming shanty towns on the fringes of the big cities. These reflect the huge discrepancies between the opportunities of first and third world peoples, both individually and collectively, to pursue lives of their own; discrepancies, that is, in their general levels of well-being, however we choose to define it. Health is not the whole of well-being, but it is unrealistic if not impossible to separate health care from wider socio-political considerations. To understand the problems of third world health, we have to reflect not only on social priorities and economic policies but also on political regimes and whole ways of life – our own included – and on how they interrelate.

*Some existing responses to the problem*

A common response to the more dramatic manifestations of third world need is to view them like any other human disaster: initially to treat them as

191

emergencies requiring a rapid response, and then to look for ways of preventing a recurrence. Most would find it natural to feel moral obligation to help others who are afflicted by extremes of hunger, epidemic disease and other calamities. Offering food, shelter and health care aid is one obvious and perfectly *ordinary* response to this obligation: the greater the suffering the more imperative the sense of having a duty to do something about it. Yet the whole subject of aid is surrounded by controversy regarding its importance and long-term value; the question of what and how much aid is required is obscured by the rather different questions of who has most responsibility for giving it and even of whether aid works at all.

Such questions are sharpened by the characteristics of population health status in many third world countries. Children are undernourished and die young; polluted water and crowded and confined living conditions mean that diseases like measles and whooping cough often kill, and that diarrhoea, polio, typhoid and cholera flourish. By contrast with the abundance of mortality and morbidity, the obvious response – effective primary health care – is in practice typically sporadic and starved of resources. Compared with the more high-flown versions of 'Health for All by the Year 2000', the objective of achieving effective primary health care for a majority of the world's population seems much more modest – yet it is further off than ever. In more specific terms, there has been no shift away from the now-established pattern of relatively advanced 'curative' medicine for the urban affluent minority at the expense of preventive medicine for the poor.

Yet in many instances it looks as if the situation could be dramatically altered by relatively inexpensive preventive measures like sewage control, vaccination programmes and the informational and advisory benefits of a robust system of primary health care workers. Is it only a lack of aid which stands in the way of adopting effective preventive measures like these? What happened to the widely endorsed aspiration of the 1978 Alma Ata Conference to promote such measures? The intention was to generalise the achievements of localised health care initiatives such as those already flourishing in parts of India and Guatemala, and most notably in the form of the community-based 'barefoot' doctors of China. But the 1980s recession in the West reduced the flow of aid and limited most third world primary health care programmes to child survival (in effect, oral rehydration and immunisation). Pressure from the World Bank and the International Monetary Fund led to the adoption of monetarist financial strategies resulting in mounting debt; and privatisation of health care has rendered primary provision if anything even less adequate. The spread of 'user-financing' and 'cost-recovery' schemes has put much health care beyond the means of those who need it most. Money which would otherwise have been spent on food is spent on commercial medicines. Among the foreseeable outcomes: an increased incidence of child malnutrition and disease; and, after a period of falling child-mortality, a rise. Currently, though now calling for increased public spending, the World Bank is still committed to promoting a US-style private health care model. Purportedly this is in the interests of cost-effectiveness and to 'promote diversity and competition in health services', despite evidence of gross ineffectiveness and of the especially adverse effects of 'diversity and competition' in contexts of acute resource scarcity where the vast bulk of the population is impoverished (Werner, 1995).

What this suggests is that many problems of third world health are compounded and some created by the blinkered socio-economic perceptions and hidden agendas of powerful western dominated financial institutions. But this of course is far from being the whole story and in any case it needs to be filled out; however there is no *neutral* vantage point from which to do this.

## The complexity of causes

A brief perusal of aid literature suggests the following might be added to any list of general causes of the persistence of poverty, hunger and disease:

1  the speed and unevenness of industrialisation and the problems of transition from rural to urban contexts;

2  natural disadvantages, in particular the frequency of flood, drought and crop failure, and/or the paucity of natural resources, often associated with insufficient economic and agricultural diversification and investment and with fluctuating terms of trade;

3  the adverse effects of imposed trade agreements (especially the General Agreement on Tariffs and Trade), augmented by the World Bank and International Monetary Fund loan policies already cited, which together facilitate the many harmful activities of transnational companies including leading pharmaceuticals and western commercial banks;

4  dubious internal political priorities such as expenditure on costly prestige projects like airport and hospital complexes (which represent outward and visible tokens of sovereign national status) at the expense of improved primary educational and health care provision;

5  endemic susceptibility to civil strife. Why and how this works as a general cause of poverty is difficult to summarise, yet it is so important that an attempt must be made. It is largely attributable to the following interconnected factors:

193

- the breakdown of traditional society and the emergence of new de-cultured, politically powerful but unaccountable elites;
- the pursuit by leaders and their emergent middle class supporters of ungeneralisable first world lifestyles, which can be sustained only at the expense of the continuing deprivation of the poor;
- the permeation of public and social life by individualistic values which work to the advantage of the already privileged and so exacerbate existing socio-economic inequalities;
- the entrenchment of divisions between rich and poor which undermine old solidarities and inhibit the formation of new, the ensuing instability favouring the emergence of authoritarian or military regimes with an interest in retaining control over access to an essentially limited number of positional goods;
- disproportionate expenditure on defence and internal security because the poor and dispossessed are (rightly) seen as lacking reason for loyalty to the incumbent regime and as natural recruits for resistance movements (and are often treated abominably as a result);
- regional superpower intervention to install or buttress ideologically 'safe' regimes or to destabilise ideologically suspect ones, seemingly regardless of their competence or popularity;
- casualties of past civil strife who include many thousands of refugees and sometimes whole population groups and cultures, whose continued demoralisation traps them in a vicious circle of bitterness and despair;

6 in the case of several states, a further set of causal complications usually linked with past colonial conquest and the lack of 'fit' between cultural and political boundaries: they are plural states without pluralist traditions to help hold them together. The resulting politics of insecurity is characterised by ineptitude, tribalism, nepotism and venality which together may deflect or hinder the best of internal nation-building and of external aid intentions.

Typically the effects of these circumstances on health status are catastrophic, in terms of infant mortality, preventable yet nonetheless endemic disease, and avoidable deaths. The prospect of indefinite continuation is an affront to human dignity which wouldn't be tolerated in the developed world. But clearly we who are born in the first world cannot be said to have earned or to deserve our advantageous situation any more than those who are born in the third world could be said to deserve their fate. The problem remains of how to explain why so much unquestionable need *continues* to go unmet. Part of the difficulty is that it often arises in circumstances so impoverished or hostile that new needs are constantly being generated, and this again poses the question of how to meet such needs without tackling their socio-economic causes and so extending the 'aid agenda' to include social and political change.

## For and against aid

A convincing case against aid of any kind seems as unlikely as one for aid of every kind. Yet as far as *government* aid is concerned there are several examples of the former, but none of the latter. The argument against depends on confining the legitimate activity of government solely to safeguarding the natural rights of its subjects. The standard counter to this appeals to a different rationale for government as the instrument of shared values and collective purposes, purposes which may amongst other things commit it to aid that helps secure the equal natural rights of strangers. We tell our government what we want it to do, which may include sending food to the starving in Africa and Asia. So far so good. But disposing of the argument against the giving of government aid in principle isn't to dispose of the case against aid.

If we ask what would count as good general reasons against aid, at least three could be given:

1  that its objects could be better achieved in some other way – for example by a re-ordering of the third world's internal priorities in favour of preventive health care;

2  that real doubt existed about the attainability, desirability or merits of its objects – doubt for example about development aid intended to improve the industrial infrastructure but premised on the expectation of indefinite expansion of international trade and the achievement of global consumerism;

3  that on balance its disadvantages are likely to outweigh any gains – for example where aid to reduce dependence on food imports by increasing agricultural self-sufficiency would raise prices beyond the means of the poor and further reduce rural employment.

### Disputing the 'best means'

Our response to arguments advanced under any of these headings will depend on the kind of aid in question; on whether we view it from a donor, recipient, or third-party perspective; on our ideological orientation; and on the assumptions we make about likely outcomes, etc. Even so, we can accept many arguments advanced under the first heading – that there are better alternative means – while rejecting such arguments' conclusiveness. We may allow that the object of relieving poverty would be better achieved by a re-allocation of internal resources; but so long as this doesn't take place a case for aid would remain, though it might then be a case for *combining* aid for the direct relief of poverty with wider aid strategies to encourage the adoption of more welfare-orientated policies. Yet we should note that what we would then be doing is re-describing the nature and object of aid, that is, modifying the case for aid rather than conceding the case against it.

Those who attach overriding importance to third world nations' defining and confronting their own problems tend to assume nations ought to be treated like self-determining individuals who at most should be encouraged to be more resilient; disasters apart, they are prone to see all but strictly limited and controlled 'development' aid as paternalistic meddling. An obvious rejoinder to this is to question the plausibility of assuming untrammelled free agency, whether of individuals or nations, and to stress certain crucial differences of kind and of circumstance. Is there good reason to doubt the relevance to the aid case of the recognition either that some are more free than others, or that for a dispossessed peasantry to be trapped in poverty is for it to be unfree even though its rulers aren't? From a first world perspective of those who see poverty and the sorry state of primary care in the third world as an affront to moral sensibility, and its continuance as a disaster, the case for effective humanitarian aid is likely to appear overwhelming – better alternative possibilities notwithstanding. So the point to reiterate here is that what we see as compelling largely depends on where we're looking from and on how we evaluate what we see. Change your assumptions or your vantage point and different conclusions are bound to follow.

*Disputing aid's goals*

This is even more clearly evident for the second category of objections to aid which relate to the attainability or merit of its objects; for whilst it's hard to doubt the worthiness of aid for relief of suffering and privation, even where we are unable to remedy their causes, it is easy to find good reason to disagree about aid for development. Development to, or for, what? For a world increasingly exercised about environmental matters in the face of rapidly diminishing natural resources, growing pollution and climatic change, the issue of development insistently prompts the questions: sustainable for how long and at what cost, both to future and to present generations? Optimists appeal to science and technology on the one hand and to industrial and market regulation on the other to take care of us; for them there is reason to support all well-considered development aid projects, that is, projects which are properly sensitive to local circumstances and which promise to promote efficient wealth-creation. Pessimists are deeply sceptical about the prospects for scientific technology and/or economic control. Here the choice lies between the more hopeful and the more despairing. But the political economy of development has difficulty in agreeing the terms of the debate. How far can there be development that is common to different societies but which nonetheless leaves them free to pursue their different ends? How can we formulate comparative measures of the quality of individual and community life?

## Weighing goods against harms

In popular discussion, many objections to aid fall into the third category, that of the balance of advantages and disadvantages. Each of these 'balance of advantage' objections expresses a quandary for the liberal, who recognises the moral claims of both the provision of benefits and the avoidance of harms. For instance, aid may allegedly produce *dependency* in recipients, by introducing a novel source of material and other goods, coupled with the expectation that this source will remain open. By so doing, it is held that aid weakens recipients' ability or alternatively their resolve to address their problems by their own efforts and resources.[1] Of course this suggestion is undermined when there simply *are* no adequate local resources: there are some lacks which no amount of local effort can overcome. Any remaining force in the objection can be countered by careful aid design, to produce self-sustaining rather than 'zero-sum' benefits.

Another objection is that aid may be characterised simply as *interference* where this is taken to be self-evidently bad, typically on the grounds that the aid changes the recipients. Of course it would be pointless if it didn't! So the question is therefore whether the relevant changes are wanted or justifiable. We could point out that international trade is also interference, especially when conducted under imposed terms. Aid changes people: but they may want to change. Cultures moreover aren't static; many are already under threat or are disintegrating as a result of the oppressive or injurious policies currently pursued internally. What's wrong, therefore, with change in the abstract? Everything depends on what the change is and on how it's achieved. For instance, change is an express aim of health education whenever it is undertaken. Moreover it seems legitimate to intend changes to policies which presently harm or injure.

A more penetrating objection to aid characterises it as *collusion* with the aims of the 'aided' parties. But one must first ask, who are the aided parties? The intention behind aid is standardly that these be victims of disaster and oppression rather than the perpetrators. The question then resolves into one

197

of aid's effectiveness in avoiding the facilitation of further objectionable use of existing resources. To take an example, governments would seem obliged to expend resources to deal with a disease epidemic; external aid which is addressed to the problem in the process relieves such governments of their own responsibility – and thus frees the relevant resources for the pursuit of irresponsible policies which perpetuate the causes of present disadvantage.

Aid can appear collusive by providing an opportunity for diversion of resources, or more fundamentally by postponing the inevitable confrontation with the underlying injustices and hence delaying radical solutions to them: in effect, applying 'poultices' to present problems thus relieving (albeit in an illusory sense) pressure for change. This charge has some substance, but it need not defeat the case for persisting with aid, because local needs themselves persist. Immediate aid is still needed while structural solutions are sought. Nor should we assume that external aid undermines the motivation for change. Indeed it would be irresponsible to concentrate exclusively on trying to bring that change about, since its complex causes might elude us, whilst present remediable need continued to go unmet. Effective remedies require understanding of the problem; but the long-term case for structural change does not defeat the short-term case for alleviating the immediate tragedy.

Many criticisms of these kinds may appear to fail because they are ultimately not criticisms of aid *as such* but rather criticisms of deficient *forms* of aid: aid which is token, ineffective, ill-aimed or wasteful. It is therefore important to see them as reasonably supporting a case against particular aid policies, strategies or objects rather than against the concept of aid as assistance to the specially needy. If we disagree with a particular type of aid or aid project then we are likely to redescribe it in the kinds of terms envisaged here, for instance not as aid but as collusion or interference.

If there were no way of helping the needy which didn't end up on balance worsening their condition, that would be the most powerful of arguments against aid. But no-one could seriously claim to demonstrate this.


## Basic needs, obligations and justice

We can hold a conception of 'needs' that has a moral entailment built into it. On this conception, in *recognising* something as a significant need in others we give expression to our moral concern that the need be met. This relationship between needs and obligations is qualified by degree: the more basic or urgent the need, the stronger the corresponding obligation. Gillon suggests that '... need creates a presumptive claim in justice or fairness such that the greater the need the greater the presumptive claim on others who have fewer needs' (1994, p.798). A parallel view invokes the idea of rights:

198

consider Griffin's (1986) notion of rights as 'value-protectors'. A substantive theory of human rights must be based on notions of personhood, the practicality of the protections required, and equal respect. These three grounds yield various human rights, including that to some form of equal share in what makes a good life possible. The key point for our purposes is that the relative importance of rights is determined by the weight of the values to which they are linked.

Undeniably the situation which prompts health care aid is one of urgent unmet need, and on the view rehearsed here, no more requires to be said in order to establish that such needs place a corresponding claim or obligation upon those of us in vastly more fortunate circumstances. However there is no agreed view of needs or of the nature and extent of the obligations they occasion. Some views of need distinguish a special class as being basic and as producing special obligations *on that account*. Since the health care needs we are considering readily fall into this special category, it is worth pursuing this distinction. One can define basic needs as those which must be met if human life under *any* tolerable description is to be sustained; then to the extent that we attach value to human life, to that extent we must also acknowledge obligations to meet such needs.

Effectively to meet basic needs in the third world presupposes, first, that being deprived of the all-purpose means to human survival is a matter of general moral concern (we mean human survival as such, and not human survival within some limiting cultural description); and, second, that there are also practical possibilities of doing so: that means can or must be found which don't in the process undermine the general structure of existing moral obligations.

What stands in the way of meeting such basic needs?

1 in philosophical terms, settling on a workable notion of basic needs; distinguishing survival needs from more sophisticated health care needs: the requirement of *defining basic needs*;

2 also in philosophical terms, discerning whether such needs entail correlative duties or obligations: the requirement of *establishing duties*;

3 if they do then, in moral terms, distinguishing the kind of duties involved, such as whose duties they be, whether they be individual or collective duties, what is their extent and so forth: principally, the requirement that we settle *the distinction between justice and charity*.

(A fourth, practical requirement is that we work out a way of meeting them without improper interference in the affairs of another state, but we must

199

postpone consideration of this until the next section.)

*Defining basic needs*

Basic needs are a class of requirements for things ('all-purpose goods') necessary to achieve widely, and highly, valued ends – such that an inability to achieve these ends seriously imperils and impoverishes one's life and well-being. Basic needs are those needs which, if not at least minimally met, produce a state that would be judged unfit for any human being to be in, from any morally plausible standpoint. We can distinguish between all-purpose basic needs and needs which are basic to survival under some *given* description, needs which accordingly vary with culture (so that electricity could feature among them in some cultures). Some would question the possibility of separating these two sorts of basic need on the ground that all needs are met in particular social contexts which each specify their own criteria of tolerable existence. An alternative view is that although no hard and fast line can be drawn in practice between what is basic to life *as such* and what is basic to this or that life, it marks as important a distinction as that between what is necessary and what is sufficient for a tolerable life.[2] We can prioritise the meeting of all-purpose needs ahead of the meeting of needs, say, for greater equality of 'life chances'.

Some physical facts about human beings seem bound to be part of any account we may give of their survival needs, and look as though they validate objective knowledge of specifiable requirements if people are to survive; such needs clearly embrace nutrition and a minimum standard of primary health care. Not all health care needs qualify as basic needs. We may accept that the case for meeting basic health care needs cannot readily be separated from the case for meeting other basic needs. But the kinds of health care needs we identified in the first section ('The problem') as relevant to the problems of third world malnutrition and disease seem central to any plausible set of basic needs. However there is real difficulty in deciding when all-purpose needs have been adequately – or at least minimally – met. As Griffin puts it: 'How much of these all-purpose means are *needed*?' (1986, p.44). Answering this question is always going to be contentious, but we think it justifiable to put it on one side on the ground that – given the extent of unequivocally urgent third world need – it will be some time before it becomes morally troubling.

*Establishing duties*

We began this section by noting the view of needs that entails moral obligation. It would seem that any view of needs would recognise that

200

sufficently serious unmet needs straightforwardly cause deep moral concern, simply on account of their seriousness. If *any* needs do this, then surely all-purpose basic needs do (such as the need for clean water). It is in this spirit that Gillon defends his account of needs as being 'consistent with normal humanitarian and medical assumptions that the most seriously ill or at risk take priority in claims upon our assistance *even if giving them that priority entails that overall welfare is not maximised*' (1994, p.798, original emphasis).

A parallel emphasis can be expressed in terms of rights. If respect for rights involves respect for everybody's rights (Barry, 1995), then a right to have one's basic needs taken seriously applies wherever they are in danger of being unmet. To take an extreme example, slavery or torture are unacceptable everywhere: why should this not be true also of malnutrition or chronic neglect? An advantage of putting the point in terms of rights is that rights can limit our natural partiality in response to what are generally agreed to be weighty collective concerns.

*Distinguishing justice from charity*

Justice can be seen principally as the procedural arbitration between rival claims, or as fairness or impartiality requiring that we treat people as equally deserving of respect. It is the latter sense of justice that concerns us here. The trouble is that aid seen as charity encourages us to view our response to the needs of others as satisfied by individual efforts on such occasions as our conscience is moved by the plight of the sufferers. But we can't make this sort of response continuously whereas the need to which it is a response, and the obligation to meet it, *are* continuous, until the need is met in some reliable way. Aid seen as justice is collectively more demanding: failings here are more obvious failings in moral duty. At an individual level we can respond to the claims of humanitarian aid only as acts of individual charity. But as citizens or as political and social agents, meeting such needs becomes a matter of *collective* duty: an issue of justice. And it is the role of government to try to curb the freedom of the strong, the fortunate, the able from being used exploitatively. Government is the instrument of common concern, whether abroad or at home.

Again, charity is what as individuals we fall back upon when collective provision is lacking or inadequate. But it is always our duty as social beings to try to ensure effective collective mechanisms of provision. There is no apparent reason for relocating the grounds of third world aid from those of justice to those of charity other than the non-existence of suitable institutions with responsibility for meeting those needs. And since we could be said to have duties to work towards establishing such institutions, it seems that their current absence or inadequacy give no persuasive reason for not regarding third world aid as a matter of justice.

It is fairly clear why we might accept a duty to establish such institutions. Within a given community, nearly everyone recognises some claims of distributive justice (a form of justice as fairness). Most people think it unjust to fail to take account of difference in means when levying taxation. Whenever people come to see themselves as belonging to a community they see themselves as sharing significant common interests and commitments, and they acknowledge reciprocal claims. Large continuous and correctable differences in quality and length of life come to be seen as matters of justice. Then we have occasion to create mechanisms for the transfer of resources.

Hence one way to make third world aid an issue of justice would be to imagine – and then take seriously – a surrogate community embracing both those needing aid and those of us who are able to offer it. But we should be clear how such a community ought to be conceived. As O'Neill (1993) has pointed out, the virtue of 'idealised' theories of justice is their impartiality: they can abstract from individual particularities and are blind to considerations of race, gender etc. – the very things that stand as obstacles to taking third world aid seriously. By contrast, 'relativised' theories of justice operate principles derived from the traditions of particular communities which typically place matters of social concern for specific groups, including disadvantaged groups, outside the acknowledged concerns of justice – thus providing no means to establish the essential unfairness of unmet basic needs among such groups. So to be of any use, a surrogate community must be imagined in whatever ways are necessary to overcome, from the very start, any such partiality against those who most need aid.

## The locus and scope of responsibility

Where lies the responsibility for meeting the claims of aid? At first sight it seems as though the answer is tied to the question of who needs the aid. In this final section we shall try to establish that in fact this is *not* where the answer should be found, and that it is the character of the need, rather than the identity or whereabouts of the needy, that determines the obligation to meet it.

### Equality of treatment and of respect

Given that the idea of aid (in the sense of assistance) seems by definition to be a morally-positive term, it makes little sense to object to the idea of aid as such; we've seen that objections to aid are inevitably objections to aid for particular recipients in particular circumstances – in other words they inevitably discriminate among, and hence evaluate, claims made upon us. The evaluation and ranking of claims involves staking out a moral position and defending it against other moral positions, above all rebutting or overcoming the standard moral presumption that people ought to be treated in the same way.

More fully, the presumption is that we should treat persons (and peoples) comparably or equally unless there is good reason to treat them otherwise. Good reasons have to be established and defended, and sceptics cannot simply assert that a good reason is constituted by (for instance) the supposed moral significance of national boundaries. That would be in effect to rely on the identity or whereabouts of the needy in order to justify differential responses, responses which are different *despite* the equivalence of need. This seems unconvincing compared with the straightforward justification of responses as proportional to need: for instance, a good reason is easily provided for the preferential treatment of women and children in terms of giving priority to the needs of the *most vulnerable*, whose needs by definition are *not* equivalent to the needs of the less vulnerable. The identity of a person or of his citizenship or nationality is widely held to be relevant to such matters as his responsibility to defend his society in time of war, and also to such legal entitlements as voting: but such considerations seem far removed from the issue of determining *who* is responsible for meeting *whose* basic needs.

*'Natural' ties and other boundaries*

Attempted justifications for discrimination based on identity will first appeal to the ties of naturally-shared identities – those of family, neighbourhood or citizenship – and then declare these to have moral content. We have an unreflective preference for those with whom we can more readily identify, because of a shared language, culture, history or faith. Barry (1991; 1995) reminds us that such moral partiality is illustrated by the belief that lives of our own fellow-nationals should not be put at risk in the service of lives of other nationals; that they count for more than the lives of other nationals, and special justification is needed for putting them at risk. It is clear enough how much moral content such preferences are taken to bear. The question is how much they *ought to* bear.

At the individual or family level the obligation to meet needs constitutes a special claim on us: obligations to which it is appropriate to make an individual response and where we are ordinarily left to judge the response as individuals. Here the intimacy of the relationship is obviously important (but even these relationships are subject to wider societal scrutiny and accountability: morality has a public dimension in both logical and practical terms).

By contrast it is unclear what moral status can be invoked merely by identifying a recipient as being a fellow-countryman. What connections do we have with people in the next street, the next town etc. which constitute sufficient grounds for according them differential or superior moral status such that when *their* needs go unmet we have an obligation to respond to them which almost invariably overrides any obligation to respond to the vastly greater needs of foreigners? Can we justify the extent of our partiality? It's not at all clear that we can.

An intermediate case might be that of shared belief systems. Imagine, for instance, Anglicans in one country who noticed that other Anglicans were suffering systematic persecution under a foreign regime and who felt a duty to go to the aid of those who shared their beliefs and suffered for it. But why should they limit such concerns to co-believers? More generally, how could we justify a differential response or concern which depended simply on considerations of the identity of the sufferers' faith, nationality, culture, gender or age – particularly when such discriminatory considerations would be outlawed *within* our own society.

It seems then that ties of this kind may *explain* our prioritising the interests of those close to us; but they do not *justify* our doing this to the exclusion of the unmet vital interests of strangers. And once we recognise this, then to suppose that the systematic use of torture is not our concern on account of its being conducted across the border becomes formally parallel to supposing that wife battering or child abuse is not our business on account of its being committed next door. And the parallels are not confined to such gross abuses. Issues of the 'fair distribution' of resources arise – and are rightly understood as such – in any large pluralistic society. How and why is this different from the situation where those issues arise *between* societies?

We must move from, in effect, according equal respect to only such persons as are fellow-citizens or fellow-nationals, or persons to whom we have some determinate obligation to respect, to respecting persons *as such*. And as Barry (1991) has convincingly argued, respecting persons as such may entail not merely not harming them but also promoting their good or their well-being so far as it falls within our power: something which seems categorically to require our attempting to respond to their unmet basic needs.

*The scope of collective action*

Initially it may be as individuals that we are moved to respond to the needs of strangers. Yet we can also be seen to respond collectively through official government aid programmes and contributions to United Nations specialist agency budgets. But where the predominant attitude to such aid is not morally ambiguous, it regards it as a kind of collective charity. So whilst we may acknowledge charitable aid duties beyond national borders, too often they tend to be treated with moral partiality as being optional or supererogatory. Yet once an obligation of justice is recognised, the scale of the need should determine the scale on which that need ought to be met. Plainly, it is only as collectives and as combinations of collectives that it is *possible* to make adequate responses of an organisational or institutional kind to meet these wider obligations of justice. And the *appropriate* response is collective too because such obligations also concern widely-shared core values whose implementation may be judged too important to be left to uncoordinated effort: the meeting of basic needs amounts to a concern of mankind, a concern for man *as man*.

Furthermore it is psychologically true that, as individuals or small groups, we find it easier to engage in moral response, to be altruistic or to forgo self-preference, if there is a general expectation that others will do the same. In itself this already suggests that our initial tendency to individualise our own moral responses to the needs of strangers ought to be superseded by our *politicising* them. But above all we should do this because it is still largely at the government level that there is access to the necessary transnational structures which are able to develop and sustain an effective response.

How far aid is in practice treated as an issue of justice depends on whether an appropriate transnational and re-distributive jurisdiction exists which can extend the effective area of juridical concern. This suggests that we may need to create, extend, or make more effective such jurisdictions. There are ample precedents for doing so, and they can arise whenever the 'surrogate communities' we envisaged in the last section are taken sufficiently seriously. For instance the European Union has evolved from an Economic Community in which commonalities of economic interest gave rise to a surrogate community. That community has large-scale re-distributive mechanisms (in particular the European Social Fund and the European Regional Development Fund) for redressing imbalances of fate and fortune within its transnational jurisdiction. The jurisdiction may have come about for other reasons, but it still illustrates the point that such things can be envisaged and created. In its train come expressly juridical institutions such as the European Court of Human Rights, at which *transnational* partiality can be remedied as a matter not of charity but of justice.

When such jurisdictions are slow to arise, how should we respond to the failure of some countries to contribute to the general aid effort? Must we 'take up the slack' left by what we see as the default of others? Within our own society there are precedents for accepting this: we cannot simply abandon children who have in fact been abandoned, abused or neglected by their own parents. By extension we may feel that to respond separately as nations is our

205

only possible course if collective transnational responses are lacking. It seems there must be limits to this. But setting them may also, and readily, be seen as an issue of justice: here the question of fairness arises in the distribution of the burden of responsibility.

*Determining governments' responsibility*

Proponents of collective aid have to contend with the still-dominant and so-called realist morality of international relations which ties the justification of aid not to need but to our own national interests and advantages, conceived of in narrowly materialistic terms. Some views might envisage a larger role for governments than that allowed under the minimal conception of the state – for instance, contrast the views of Rawls (1972) and of Nozick (1974) – yet might still incline to limit welfare concerns to the state's own citizens on the grounds of its holding specific responsibilities to act for *their* well-being and interests, making it *ultra vires* to act otherwise. Several different responses are possible to such a view. But on a larger view of interests which incorporated, say, an interest in promoting human rights it might actually *be* in that state's interests to offer aid. Again, on an instrumental view of government its job would be to pursue whatever goals are set by the electorate, so if the electorate decides it wants the government to pursue general humanitarian objectives the problems reduce to practicalities. Perhaps the most committed response is also finally the most convincing: all governments (and all states) ultimately share a common interest in addressing humanitarian aid concerns on a global level. But the responsibility at least of western liberal governments, as agents of community values and in particular of justice-as-impartiality, needn't and shouldn't stop here. It extends to making much more strenuous efforts to tackle the *causes* of the problem of persistent and urgent unmet need with which we began. This would involve such things as greater commitment to securing fairer terms of trade for the third world and finding more effective ways of regulating armaments and arms trade, of rendering transnational corporations accountable and of monitoring the long-term effects of the loan and investment policies of major financial institutions. Above all there needs to be a greater willingness to enquire into the nature and causes of the *unequal* wealth of nations.[3]

### Acknowledgement

I am greatly indebted to the editors for their forbearance; but most of all to Martyn Evans who, at the eleventh hour, transformed and enriched an assortment of inchoate jottings into a - hopefully - coherent narrative. Without

206

his very generous help this chapter would not have been written.

## Notes

1. Similarly aid may be seen as having what insurance companies refer to as the 'moral hazard effect', namely that it renders recipients less likely to avoid getting into the situation aid is intended to relieve.

2. This is very similar to Griffin's view of basic needs as 'needs for the all-purpose means to whatever ends different individuals may choose... they connect with ends we do not choose but which are characteristic of human existence. Each of us chooses his own life plan; none of us chooses *the sorts of things that are necessary for living out any life plan*' (Griffin, 1986, pp.43-4, italics added).

3. The allusion here of course is to Adam Smith's *An Enquiry Into the Nature and Causes of the Wealth of Nations* first published in 1776.

## Bibliography

Barry, B. (1991), *Liberty and Justice*, Oxford University Press, Oxford.
Barry, B. (1995), *Justice as Impartiality*, Oxford University Press, Oxford.
Gillon, R. (ed.) (1994), *Principles of Health Care Ethics*, John Wiley, Chichester.
Griffin, J. (1986), *Well-Being*, Oxford University Press, Oxford.
Nozick, R. (1974), *Anarchy, State, and Utopia*, Basil Blackwell, Oxford.
O'Neill, O. (1993), 'Justice, gender and international boundaries', in Nussbaum, M. and Sen, A. (eds), *The Quality of Life*, Oxford University Press, Oxford.
Rawls, J. (1972), *A Theory of Justice*, Oxford University Press, Oxford and New York.
Werner, D. (1995), 'Who killed primary healthcare?', *New Internationalist*, No. 272.